Middle Level C
Student Language Book

Bridge to Communication ELEPS

A program of English for Limited English Proficient students, based on material developed and field-tested by the Second Language Education Department of the San Diego Unified School District

Santillana Publishing Company

Content Editor/Author of Student Work Sheets
Nancy Sokol Green

Contributing Editors
Sandra Plaskon
Teresa Walter

Student Language Book. ©1992 by Santillana Publishing Company.
Revised edition ©1991 by Santillana Publishing Company.
Original edition ©1985 by San Diego Unified School District.

ISBN: 1-56014-259-6

Printed in the United States of America.

Santillana Publishing Company, Inc.
901 West Walnut Street, Compton, CA 90220

91 92 93 94 95 96 6 5 4 3 2 1

San Diego Unified School District

Principal Author
Sandra Plaskon
Project Resource Teacher
Primary Grades ELEPS Team Leader

Contributing Editors
Janet Delaney
Project Resource Teacher

Sheila Oberst
Project Resource Teacher

Teresa Walter
Project Resource Teacher

Project Supervisors
Tim Allen
Director of Second Language Education

Linda Valladolid
Curriculum Coordinator for Second Language Education

Consultants
Dr. Robert A. Bennett, Director
San Diego Unified School District
Programs Division

Dr. Charles H. Herbert, President
Checkpoint Systems, Inc.

Dr. Natalie Kuhlman
Professor of Education
San Diego State University

Dr. Adel Nadeau, Consultant
Bilingual Education Office
San Diego Unified School District

Harold B. Wingard
Director of Basic Education
San Diego Unified School District

Grateful acknowledgement is given to the following San Diego Unified School District staff members who contributed to the original ELEPS program: the many teachers who participated in program development and field-testing and the editors, word processors, and artists who produced program materials.

CONTENTS

A Note to the Teacher

STUDENT WORK SHEETS

■ **Unit 1: Mapping It Out**

Student Work Sheet 1.1
Student Work Sheet 1.2
Student Work Sheet 1.3
Student Work Sheet 1.4
Student Work Sheet 1.5
Student Work Sheet 1.6

■ **Unit 2: Exploring New Frontiers**

Student Work Sheet 2.1
Student Work Sheet 2.2
Student Work Sheet 2.3
Student Work Sheet 2.4
Student Work Sheet 2.5
Student Work Sheet 2.6

■ **Unit 3: Telling Tall Tales**

Student Work Sheet 3.1
Student Work Sheet 3.2
Student Work Sheet 3.3
Student Work Sheet 3.4
Student Work Sheet 3.5
Student Work Sheet 3.6

■ **Unit 4: America: A Nation of Immigrants**

Student Work Sheet 4.1
Student Work Sheet 4.2
Student Work Sheet 4.3
Student Work Sheet 4.4
Student Work Sheet 4.5
Student Work Sheet 4.6

■ **Unit 5: America's Finest**

Student Work Sheet 5.1
Student Work Sheet 5.2
Student Work Sheet 5.3
Student Work Sheet 5.4
Student Work Sheet 5.5
Student Work Sheet 5.6

■ **Unit 6: We the People**

Student Work Sheet 6.1
Student Work Sheet 6.2
Student Work Sheet 6.3
Student Work Sheet 6.4
Student Work Sheet 6.5
Student Work Sheet 6.6

■ **Unit 7: The Art of Science**

Student Work Sheet 7.1
Student Work Sheet 7.2
Student Work Sheet 7.3
Student Work Sheet 7.4
Student Work Sheet 7.5
Student Work Sheet 7.6

■ **Unit 8: Mysteries of the Deep**

Student Work Sheet 8.1
Student Work Sheet 8.2
Student Work Sheet 8.3
Student Work Sheet 8.4
Student Work Sheet 8.5
Student Work Sheet 8.6

■ **Unit 9: Weather Watch**

Student Work Sheet 9.1
Student Work Sheet 9.2
Student Work Sheet 9.3
Student Work Sheet 9.4
Student Work Sheet 9.5
Student Work Sheet 9.6

■ **Unit 10: Searching the Solar System**

Student Work Sheet 10.1
Student Work Sheet 10.2
Student Work Sheet 10.3
Student Work Sheet 10.4
Student Work Sheet 10.5
Student Work Sheet 10.6

Unit 11: Adventures in Mythology

Student Work Sheet 11.1
Student Work Sheet 11.2
Student Work Sheet 11.3
Student Work Sheet 11.4
Student Work Sheet 11.5
Student Work Sheet 11.6

Unit 12: A World of Values

Student Work Sheet 12.1
Student Work Sheet 12.2
Student Work Sheet 12.3
Student Work Sheet 12.4
Student Work Sheet 12.5
Student Work Sheet 12.6

FOCUS SHEETS

Unit 1: Mapping It Out

Focus Sheet 1.2
Focus Sheet 1.3
Focus Sheet 1.4
Focus Sheet 1.5
Focus Sheet 1.6a
Focus Sheet 1.6b

Unit 2: Exploring New Frontiers

Focus Sheet 2.2a
Focus Sheet 2.2b
Focus Sheet 2.3a
Focus Sheet 2.3b
Focus Sheet 2.5

Unit 3: Telling Tall Tales

Focus Sheet 3.1a
Focus Sheet 3.1b
Focus Sheet 3.1c
Focus Sheet 3.1d
Focus Sheet 3.1e
Focus Sheet 3.1f
Focus Sheet 3.3a
Focus Sheet 3.3b
Focus Sheet 3.3c
Focus Sheet 3.3d
Focus Sheet 3.4

Unit 4: America: A Nation of Immigrants

Focus Sheet 4.2a
Focus Sheet 4.2b
Focus Sheet 4.4

Unit 5: America's Finest

Focus Sheet 5.1
Focus Sheet 5.2a
Focus Sheet 5.2b
Focus Sheet 5.3a
Focus Sheet 5.3b
Focus Sheet 5.4a
Focus Sheet 5.4b
Focus Sheet 5.4c
Focus Sheet 5.4d
Focus Sheet 5.4e
Focus Sheet 5.4f
Focus Sheet 5.6

Unit 6: We the People

Focus Sheet 6.1
Focus Sheet 6.3
Focus Sheet 6.5
Focus Sheet 6.6

Unit 7: The Art of Science

Focus Sheet 7.1
Focus Sheet 7.2
Focus Sheet 7.3
Focus Sheet 7.5a
Focus Sheet 7.5b
Focus Sheet 7.6a
Focus Sheet 7.6b
Focus Sheet 7.6c
Focus Sheet 7.6d

Unit 8: Mysteries of the Deep

Focus Sheet 8.2
Focus Sheet 8.3
Focus Sheet 8.4a
Focus Sheet 8.4b
Focus Sheet 8.4c
Focus Sheet 8.4d
Focus Sheet 8.5

■ Unit 9 : Weather Watch

Focus Sheet 9.2a
Focus Sheet 9.2b
Focus Sheet 9.3
Focus Sheet 9.4
Focus Sheet 9.5a
Focus Sheet 9.5b
Focus Sheet 9.5c
Focus Sheet 9.6

■ Unit 10: Searching the Solar System

Focus Sheet 10.2
Focus Sheet 10.3
Focus Sheet 10.5a
Focus Sheet 10.5b
Focus Sheet 10.5c
Focus Sheet 10.5d

■ Unit 11: Adventures in Mythology

Focus Sheet 11.1
Focus Sheet 11.2a
Focus Sheet 11.2b
Focus Sheet 11.2c
Focus Sheet 11.2d
Focus Sheet 11.2e
Focus Sheet 11.2f
Focus Sheet 11.4a
Focus Sheet 11.4b
Focus Sheet 11.4c
Focus Sheet 11.4d
Focus Sheet 11.4e
Focus Sheet 11.4f
Focus Sheet 11.4g
Focus Sheet 11.4h

■ Unit 12: A World of Values

Focus Sheet 12.2

A Note to the Teacher

This *Student Language Book* provides you the opportunity to have your students develop, practice, and apply the language and concepts presented in each lesson of BRIDGE TO COMMUNICATION. Students are expected to record their reactions, opinions, and answers in the spaces provided, and should be encouraged to participate fully in the interactive situations that this book creates.

Included in this *Student Language Book* are two types of activities: Student Work Sheets and Focus Sheets.

The primary purpose of the Student Work Sheets is to develop oral language proficiency. Many of the sheets require that students work in pairs, and that they share and discuss with others personal opinions and experiences. Many of the activities are intentionally open-ended in order to increase the opportunities for language, critical thinking, and creativity to develop. Once completed, the Student Work Sheets should be discussed as part of the Warm-Up in the subsequent lesson, hence facilitating positive student interaction with each other in the target language.

The directions for the students should be explained and modeled to ensure successful participation, and students should be encouraged to provide multiple answers. Where written answers are required, the emphasis should be on communication of ideas rather than on correctness of spelling, syntax and grammar.

The Focus Sheets, located after the Student Work Sheets in this book, are designed for specific lesson-related tasks to be performed as directed by the teacher during the Focus segment of a lesson. Through the use of the Focus Sheets students participate in various activities, including creating story booklets and visuals for a variety of purposes. Not every lesson requires a Focus Sheet, but some lessons require more than one.

All the sheets in this book are numbered to correspond with both the unit and the lesson to which they relate. Student Work Sheet 3.4, for example, is used in the fourth lesson of Unit 3. If more than one sheet is needed in a lesson, lowercase letters indicate the sequence. For example, Focus Sheets 4.1a, 4.1b, and 4.1c are all used in the first lesson of Unit 4. Focus Sheets in the back of this book are perforated so that your students may tear them out to facilitate cutting. If so desired, you may also tear out the Student Work Sheets, but keep in mind that the activities on the front and back of each sheet are not necessarily done at the same time.

Middle Level C
Student Work Sheets

Help Wanted: Cartographer

■ Your new mapmaking company needs a cartographer. Write an ad for the employment section of the newspaper. Include the following in your advertisement: qualifications, job responsibilities, and salary.

Salary negotiable. Call Mrs. Jones: 338-0567.

_____
_____
_____
_____
_____
_____
_____
_____
_____
_____

Cafeteria worker. Responsible for putting food

Purpose: Content Skill/Concept Development. *Answers will vary.*

Name _____

Map Beginnings

■ Use your imagination to answer the questions.

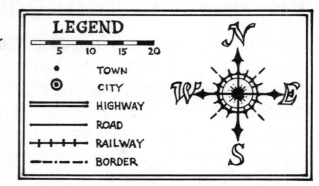

LEGEND

| 5 | 10 | 15 | 20 |

• TOWN
◉ CITY
━━━━ HIGHWAY
──── ROAD
+++++ RAILWAY
─·─·─ BORDER

1. How do you think the term <u>compass rose</u> got its name?

_____

_____

_____

_____

_____

_____

_____

2. Why do you think the box with symbols for a map is called the <u>legend</u>?

_____

_____

_____

_____

_____

_____

_____

On a Deserted Island

■ With your partner , decide on 5 famous people that you would like to have on a deserted island with you. Write ✐ each person's name and the reasons why you selected him or her.

Person 1 _____

Reasons: _____

_____

Person 2 _____

Reasons: _____

_____

Person 3 _____

Reasons: _____

_____

Person 4 _____

Reasons: _____

_____

Person 5 _____

Reasons: _____

_____

Purpose: Language Development, Critical/Creative Thinking. **Answers will vary.**

Two Kinds of Scales

■ How are a scale for weight and a scale on a map alike? How are they different? List their similarities and differences

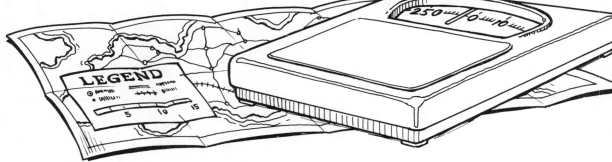

LEGEND

5   10   15

Purpose: Content Skill/Concept Development. Critical/Creative Thinking. *Answers will vary.*

Similarities

_____

_____

_____

_____

_____

Differences

_____

_____

_____

_____

_____

Mapping New Territory

■ Below is the boundary of an imaginary country. Name the country. Then draw ✎ a symbol for each landform or other item listed in the key. Draw symbols on the map to show where the features are located, including the capital city (and its name). Add the names of other countries or bodies of water that form the boundary lines for this country.

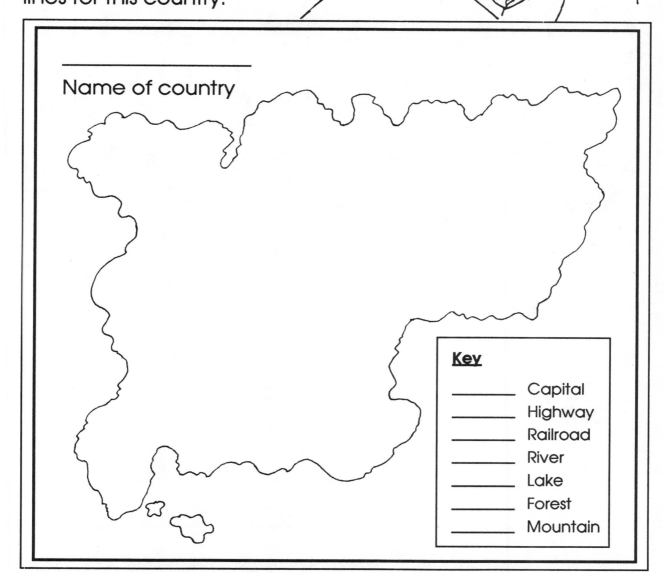

_____
Name of country

Key
_____ Capital
_____ Highway
_____ Railroad
_____ River
_____ Lake
_____ Forest
_____ Mountain

Purpose: Language Development, Content Skill/Concept Development, Critical/Creative Thinking. *Answers will vary.*

Name _____

Ranking Natural Resources

■ With your partner , decide which of these natural resources is the most important. Write the number 1 beside it. Continue ranking the others from 2 through 6.

☐ Petroleum   ☐ Iron ore   ☐ Coal

☐ Copper   ☐ Gold   ☐ Wood

■ Write 3 reasons why you believe your number 1 choice is so important.

1. _____

   _____

2. _____

   _____

3. _____

   _____

Explorers from Another Planet

■ Write ✏ 5 reasons why explorers from another planet might want to visit Earth.

1. _____

_____

2. _____

_____

3. _____

_____

4. _____

_____

5. _____

_____

Purpose: Critical/Creative Thinking. *Answers will vary.*

Name _____

Three Choices

■ You have discovered a magic
land with a mountain of gold, a
fountain of youth, and enough
food to feed the whole world.
But you can take only one of
these treasures with you.

With your partner , decide which treasure you would
choose. Then write  the reasons for your choice.

Mountain of gold	Fountain of youth	Food to feed the world

We would choose _____

because _____

_____

_____

_____

_____

_____

_____

Purpose: Language Development. Critical/Creative Thinking. **Answers will vary.**

Middle Level C

Name _____

Rules for a New Planet

■ As space explorers, you and your partner  have discovered a planet just like Earth, but it has no pollution and no people. Write ✏ a set of rules for visitors, to keep the planet clean, beautiful, and healthy.

_____

_____

_____

_____

_____

_____

_____

_____

_____

_____

_____

Purpose: Language Development, Critical/Creative Thinking. *Answers will vary.*

Middle Level C

Explorer or Pioneer?

■ Do you think it would be more difficult to be an explorer or a pioneer? Write  your answer and reasons below.

I think it would be more difficult to be _____

because _____

_____

_____

_____

_____

_____

_____

_____

_____

Name _____

Whose Job Is Harder?

■ With your partner 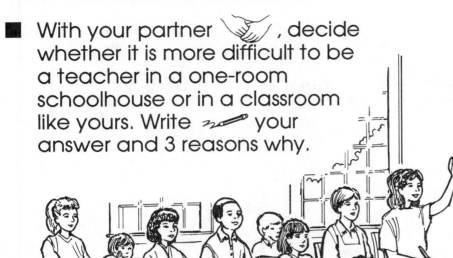, decide whether it is more difficult to be a teacher in a one-room schoolhouse or in a classroom like yours. Write ✎ your answer and 3 reasons why.

I think it would be more difficult to be a teacher in a

_____

Reason 1: _____

_____

_____

Reason 2: _____

_____

_____

Reason 3: _____

_____

_____

Purpose: Language Development, Content Skill/Concept Development. *Answers will vary.*

Name _____

Making Headlines

■ With your partner ,
write 🖊 a newspaper article
that tells the details of your
discovery. Draw 🖍 a picture
of you and your partner.

EXCITING DISCOVERY

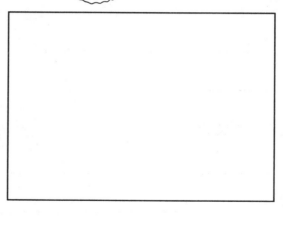

_____

_____

_____

_____

_____

_____

_____

_____

_____

_____

School Exaggerations

■ Write ✏ 2 sentences about each person listed. On the first line, write a factual sentence. On the second line, write the sentence with an exaggeration similar to those used in tall tales.

Example: Teacher

My teacher reads books quickly.

My teacher reads 69 books an hour.

Nurse

_____

_____

Custodian

_____

_____

Principal

_____

_____

Secretary

_____

_____

© Santillana Publishing Co., Inc.

Purpose: Critical/Creative Thinking. **Answers will vary.**

Name _____

Small Paul

■ Practically everyone knows
about the legendary Paul Bunyan,
but few people know about one
very strange day in Paul's life.
Write ✎ what happened on
that day and why.

Purpose: Content Skill/Concept Development. Critical/Creative Thinking. *Answers will vary.*

The Day Paul Bunyan Shrank

_____

_____

_____

_____

_____

_____

_____

_____

_____

_____

_____

Joe Magarac Headlines

■ Ever since Joe Magarac was a
baby, he has made news.
Write ✏ a headline about
Joe for each year listed. The first
one has been done for you.

Example: 1 year old

 Baby Lifts Car With One Hand! _____

3 years old

 _____

10 years old

 _____

20 years old

 _____

■ Pick one of the headlines above and write ✏ a
newspaper story about it.

_____

_____

_____

_____

_____

_____

Purpose: Language Development. Content Skill/Concept Development. Critical/Creative Thinking. *Answers will vary.*

Fun for Paul and Joe

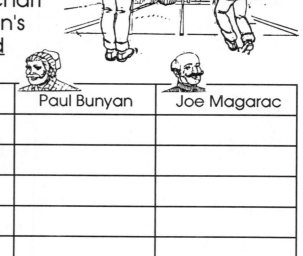

■ With your partner ✍ decide if the activities below would be appealing to Paul and Joe. Complete the chart by marking an X under the person's name if you agree that he <u>would</u> enjoy the activity.

Activity		Paul Bunyan	Joe Magarac
Camping in the woods			
Dancing at a party			
Singing in the rain			
Riding a motorcycle			
Eating in a restaurant			
Going fishing			
Making a cake			

■ Review your chart to answer the following questions.

1. Do you think Paul and Joe would like the same activities? Why or why not?

_____

_____

2. What kind of activities would <u>not</u> appeal to Paul? Why?

_____

_____

3. What kind of activities would <u>not</u> appeal to Joe? Why?

_____

_____

Name _____

Help Wanted: Tall Tale Writer

■ Write ✎ a want ad for a
tall tale writer. Include all the
necessary qualifications.

Help Wanted: Tall Tale Writer

_____

_____

_____

_____

_____

_____

_____

_____

_____

_____

_____

_____

_____

_____

_____

Purpose: Critical/Creative Thinking. _Answers will vary._

Literature Rankings

■ With your partner , decide which type of literature you prefer to read. Write ✎ the number 1 for your first choice. Continue ranking the others 2–5.

■ Write 3 reasons why you prefer your first choice.

Reason 1: _____

_____

_____

Reason 2: _____

_____

_____

Reason 3: _____

_____

_____

© Santillana Publishing Co., Inc.

Why They Came

■ Through the years, millions of people have immigrated to the United States. With your partner , write 3 reasons why you think the early immigrants came to this country.

Reason 1:

_____

_____

_____

Reason 2:

_____

_____

_____

Reason 3:

_____

_____

_____

Purpose: Language Development. Content Skill/Concept Development. Critical/Creative Thinking. *Answers will vary.*

Name _____

Willing and Unwilling

■ With your partner , think of ways the willing and unwilling immigrants were alike and different. Write ✐ your responses in the diagram.

Willing
Immigrants

_____

Alike

Unwilling
Immigrants

Purpose: Language Development, Content Skill/Concept Development, Critical/Creative Thinking. *Answers will vary.*

Middle Level C

Name _____

A Letter Home

■ You have just arrived in America. Write  a letter to your friend in your home country. Describe your voyage and first few days in America.

Purpose: Language Development, Content Skill/Concept Development, Critical/Creative Thinking. *Answers will vary.*

_____

_____

_____

_____

_____

_____

_____

_____

_____

_____

Chinese and Irish Immigrants

■ With your partner 🤝, think
of ways the Chinese and Irish
immigrants were alike and
different. Write ✏ your
responses in the diagram.

Purpose: Language Development. Content Skill/Concept Development. Critical/Creative Thinking. **Answers will vary.**

Chinese
Immigrants

Alike

Irish
Immigrants

Today's Immigrants

■ People from all over the world still want to live in the United States. Write 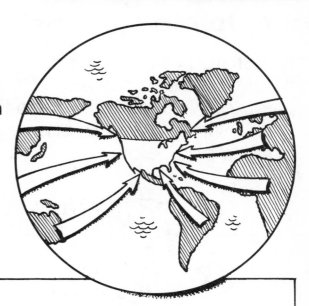 a paragraph describing one reason why you think today's immigrants want to come to this country. Draw a picture to illustrate your paragraph.

Purpose: Language Development. Content Skill/Concept Development. Critical/Creative Thinking. *Answers will vary.*

_____

_____

_____

_____

_____

Name _____

Your Opinion

Purpose: Language Development, Content Skill/Concept Development, Critical/Creative Thinking. *Answers will vary.*

■ The Statue of Liberty means many different things to different people. What does it mean to you? Write  your answer on the lines below.

_____

_____

_____

_____

_____

_____

■ Find 2 people who agree with you and write their names.

1. _____

2. _____

Something Wonderful

■ With your partner  , make
a list of 5 wonderful things the
President of the United States
could do that would make him
or her famous.

NEWSPAPER
THE PRESIDENT
SUCCEEDS!

1. _____

_____

2. _____

_____

3. _____

_____

4. _____

_____

5. _____

_____

Purpose: Language Development, Critical/Creative Thinking. *Answers will vary.*

What Would Harriet Say?

■ With your partner , decide what Harriet Beecher Stowe would write about if she were alive today. Write ✎ your ideas on the lines below.

● Name _____

We Had Dreams Too

■ Martin Luther King, Jr. had a dream that all people would someday live in peace and friendship with one another. What do you think the dreams of Susan B. Anthony, Harriet Tubman, and Cesar Chavez would be? Draw ✏️ or write ✏️ your answers.

"I have a dream...."

Susan B. Anthony

Cesar Chavez

Harriet Tubman

_____
_____
_____
_____
_____
_____
_____
_____
_____
_____

Name _____

A Dark and Silent World

■ Make a list of 10 things you did today. Then mark an X on the line to show how well you could do each thing if you could not hear or see.

	Could Still Do It	Would Need Help to Do It	Could Not Do It at All
1. _____	____	____	____
2. _____	____	____	____
3. _____	____	____	____
4. _____	____	____	____
5. _____	____	____	____
6. _____	____	____	____
7. _____	____	____	____
8. _____	____	____	____
9. _____	____	____	____
10. _____	____	____	____

Purpose: Critical/Creative Thinking. *Answers will vary.*

How Difficult?

■ With your partner , rank Helen Keller's accomplishments according to how difficult you think they were for her. Write 1 for the least difficult and rank the others 2–5, with 5 being the most difficult.

Learning to read Braille _____

Learning to make sounds _____

Graduating from college _____

Writing books _____

Presenting lectures _____

■ Which did you think was the most difficult? Explain the reasons for your choice.

_____

_____

_____

_____

Purpose: Language Development. *Answers will vary.*

I Know What I Like

■ Number the pictures in order, from the one you like most (1)
to the one you like least (4).

■ Write ✎ why you like your first choice. _____

_____

Constitutional Terms

■ What do these words from the
Constitution mean? Write
your definition for each word.

Justice: _____

_____

_____

Tranquility: _____

_____

_____

Posterity: _____

_____

_____

Select one of the words above and write ✏ its dictionary
definition.

Word: _____ Definition: _____

_____

_____

Purpose: Language Development. Content Skill/Concept Development. *Answers will vary.*

Name _____

Important Rights

■ Which of the rights guaranteed by the First Amendment to the Constitution do you think is the most important? Write  your answer. Then write 3 reasons for your choice.

Freedom of Religion

Freedom of Speech and Press

Freedom of Assembly

The most important right is: _____

_____

Reason 1: _____

_____

Reason 2: _____

_____

Reason 3: _____

_____

■ Write the name of someone who agrees with your choice.

_____

Purpose: Language Development. Content Skill/Concept Development. *Answers will vary.*

Middle Level C

● Name _____

Let's Vote!

■ With your partner , identify the 5 best arguments for and against children having the right to vote. Write ✐ your reasons.

Purpose: Language Development. Content Skill/Concept Development. Critical/Creative Thinking. *Answers will vary.*

Children <u>should</u> have the right to vote	Children <u>should not</u> have the right to vote
1. _____ _____	1. _____ _____
2. _____ _____	2. _____ _____
3. _____ _____	3. _____ _____
4. _____ _____	4. _____ _____
5. _____ _____	5. _____ _____

● ■ What is your opinion? (Circle your answer.)

Children <u>should</u> or <u>should not</u> have the right to vote.

Domestic Problems

■ With your partner ✋, think of
3 problems that you would like
the leaders of the United States
to solve. Draw 🖍 or write ✏
the problems.

Problem 1

Problem 2

Problem 3

Congressional Duties

■ Listed below are the major duties of a member of Congress. With your partner  , rank the duties in order of importance, from 1 (most important) to 6 (least important).

___ Borrow money

___ Collect taxes

___ Declare war

___ Establish post offices

___ Make laws

___ Spend money

■ Which duty do you think is the most important?

_____

Why? _____

_____

_____

Purpose: Language Development, Content Skill/Concept Development, Critical/Creative Thinking. *Answers will vary.*

Name _____

How Old Are the Presidents?

■ Use the information below to graph how old these men were when they <u>first</u> became President of the United States.

President	Age	President	Age	President	Age
Washington	57	Buchanan	65	Harding	55
J. Adams	62	Lincoln	52	Coolidge	51
Jefferson	57	A. Johnson	56	Hoover	54
Madison	54	Grant	46	F.D. Roosevelt	51
Monroe	58	Hayes	54	Truman	60
J.Q. Adams	57	Garfield	49	Eisenhower	62
Jackson	62	Arthur	50	Kennedy	43
Van Buren	54	Cleveland	47	L.B. Johnson	55
W.H. Harrison	68	B. Harrison	55	Nixon	56
Tyler	51	McKinley	54	Ford	61
Polk	49	T. Roosevelt	42	Carter	52
Taylor	64	Taft	51	Reagan	69
Fillmore	50	Wilson	56	Bush	64
Pierce	48				

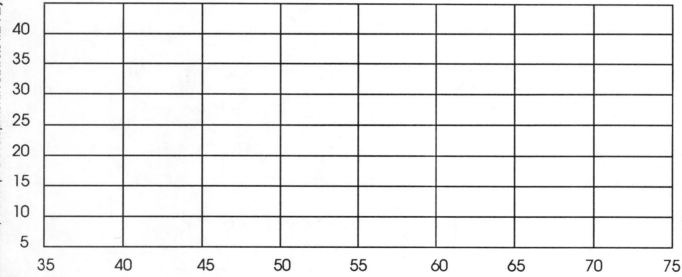

Purpose: Content Skill/Concept Development. *Answers will vary.*

■ Look at your graph.

How many presidents were 55 or younger when they took office? _____

How many presidents were older than 55 when they took office? _____

Name _____

Classroom Decor

■ With your partner , decide how you would organize the classroom furniture if you were the teacher. Draw ✏️ your new room arrangement.

Purpose: Language Development. Critical/Creative Thinking. *Answers will vary.*

Name _____

How Are They Related?

■ With your partner , decide
how the items below are related.
Write your answers on the lines.

1. How is an egg related to a chicken?

   _____

   _____

2. How is a penny related to a nickel?

   _____

   _____

3. How is a tire related to a car?

   _____

   _____

4. How is a carrot related to a rabbit?

   _____

   _____

5. How is a pencil related to a tree?

   _____

   _____

6. How is a caterpillar related to a
   butterfly?

   _____

   _____

Middle Level C

The Discovery of Borgosaurus

■ Scientists have just discovered a new dinosaur they call *Borgosaurus*. With your partner , make some inferences about this dinosaur, based on its skeleton.

1. Was it a meat-eater or a plant-eater? _____

   How do you know? _____

   _____

2. Did it walk, swim, or fly? _____

   How do you know? _____

   _____

3. Was it large or small? _____

   How do you know? _____

   _____

4. How many legs did it have? _____

   How do you know? _____

   _____

5. Did it have a tail? _____

   How do you know? _____

   _____

Purpose: Language Development, Content Skill/Concept Development. *Answers will vary.*

Name _____

The Amazing Pencil

■ With your partner ✊, think of as many applications for a pencil as you can. Write ✏️ or draw 🖍️ your ideas.

1	2
3	4
5	6
7	8

Scientists All

■ With your partner , decide which field of science you think is the most important to each of these occupations. Write the name of each occupation in the correct circle.

Rancher

Nurse

Gold miner

TV technician

Astronaut

Landscaper

TV weather reporter

Physical Science

Auto mechanic

Veterinarian

Life Science

Earth/ Space Science

Purpose: Language Development, Content Skill/Concept Development. **Answers will vary.**

A Career I Love

■ Select a science career that you think you would enjoy. Write a letter to convince a friend that your career is the best.

Purpose: Critical/Creative Thinking. *Answers will vary.*

Name _____

The Ocean Floor

■ You are a famous oceanographer on an expedition to study the ocean floor. Draw  what you see. Then write a paragraph describing your observations.

_____
_____
_____

Purpose: Language Development. Content Skill/Concept Development. Critical/Creative Thinking. *Answers will vary.*

Alphabetical Organizing

■ Help this oceanographer
organize these ocean animals
by listing them in alphabetical
order from 1 to 8.

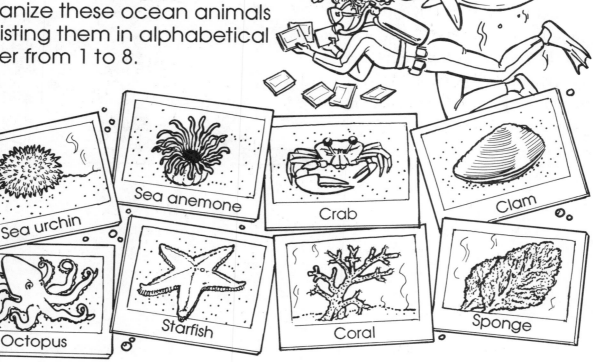

Sea urchin

Sea anemone

Crab

Clam

Octopus

Starfish

Coral

Sponge

1. _____   5. _____

2. _____   6. _____

3. _____   7. _____

4. _____   8. _____

■ Write ✎ a sentence about each animal.

1. _____

2. _____

3. _____

4. _____

5. _____

6. _____

7. _____

8. _____

Purpose: Language Development, Content Skill/Concept Development, Critical/Creative Thinking. *Answers will vary.*

Middle Level C

An Interesting Fish

■ Which of the fish you have studied is the most interesting to you? Write ✐ its name and explain why you think it is interesting. (You may also draw a picture of the fish beside its name, to help show why it is interesting.)

● Name of fish: _____

Why it is interesting: _____

_____

_____

_____

_____

_____

_____

_____

■ Find 2 other people who chose the same fish. Write ✐ their names on the lines.

● 1. _____

2. _____

Purpose: Language Development. Content Skill/Concept Development. Critical/Creative Thinking. *Answers will vary.*

A Whale of an Interview

■ The blue whale is the largest animal on earth. Interview a blue whale by asking the following questions. Then write ✏ what you think the whale's answers would be.

Question 1: How does it feel to be the largest animal on earth?

_____

_____

Question 2: What things frighten you? Why?

_____

_____

Question 3: What things make you happy?

_____

_____

Question 4: If you could be any land animal on earth, which one would you be? Why?

_____

_____

Question 5: What do you want people to know about you?

_____

_____

Purpose: Language Development, Critical/Creative Thinking. *Answers will vary.*

I Would Rather Be a ...

■ Would you rather be a whale or
a shark? Write  your answer
to complete the sentence below.
Then write a paragraph telling
why you selected that animal
and describing what kind of
whale or shark you would be.

I would rather be a _____ . Let me tell you why:

_____

_____

_____

_____

_____

_____

_____

_____

_____

_____

_____

_____

_____

_____

_____

Purpose: Language Development, Content Skill/Concept Development, Critical/Creative Thinking. *Answers will vary.*

Graphing Whales

■ Write ✏️ the names of the whales on the lines in order, from the smallest to largest. Then shade in the graph to show the length of each whale.

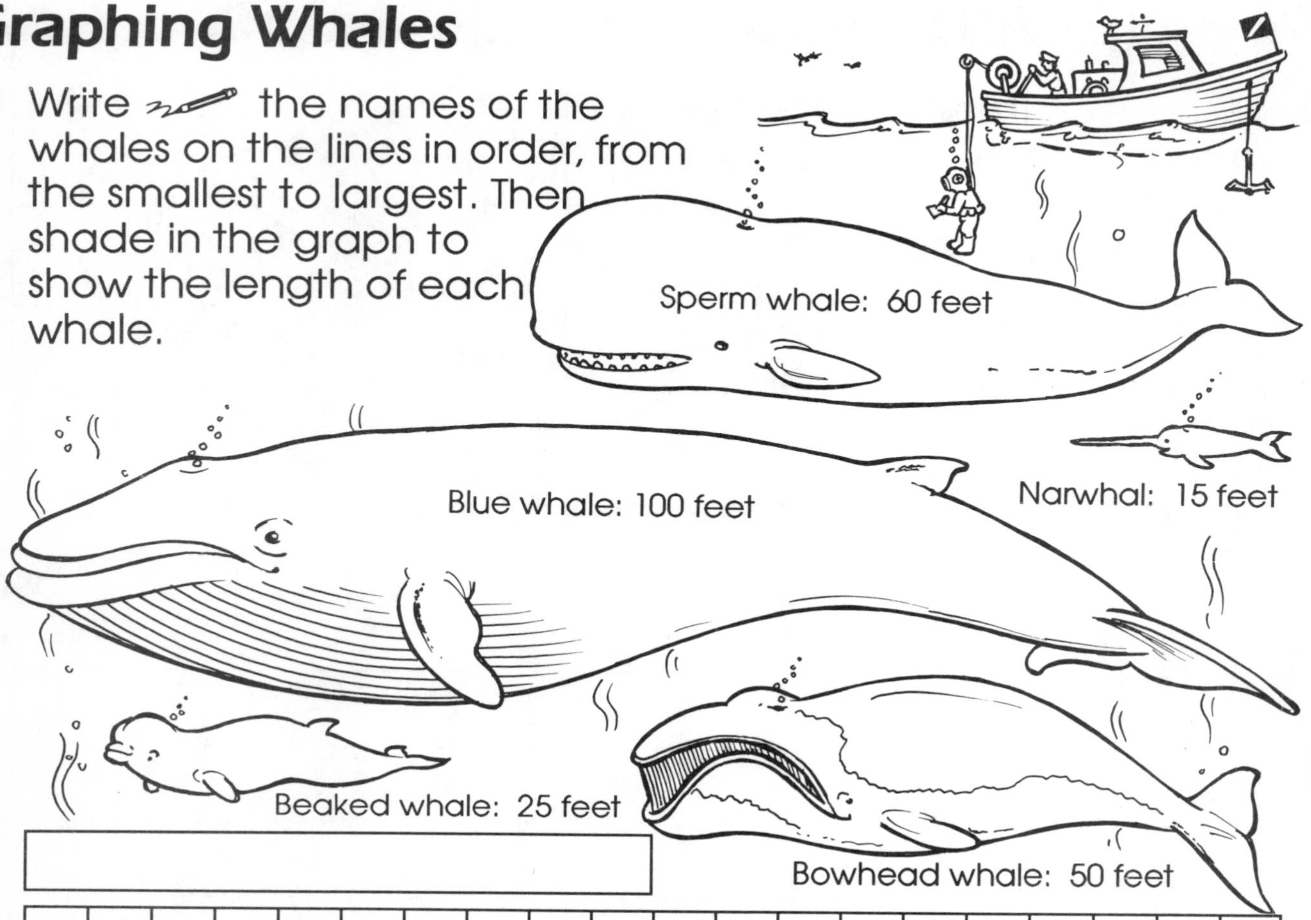

Sperm whale: 60 feet

Blue whale: 100 feet

Narwhal: 15 feet

Beaked whale: 25 feet

Bowhead whale: 50 feet

0	5	10	15	20	25	30	35	40	45	50	55	60	65	70	75	80	85	90	95	100

0	5	10	15	20	25	30	35	40	45	50	55	60	65	70	75	80	85	90	95	100

0	5	10	15	20	25	30	35	40	45	50	55	60	65	70	75	80	85	90	95	100

0	5	10	15	20	25	30	35	40	45	50	55	60	65	70	75	80	85	90	95	100

0	5	10	15	20	25	30	35	40	45	50	55	60	65	70	75	80	85	90	95	100

Middle Level C

Name _____

Words for All Seasons

■ List 5 words that describe each season.

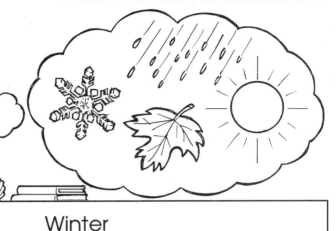

Summer	Winter
_____	_____
_____	_____
_____	_____
_____	_____
_____	_____

Fall	Spring
_____	_____
_____	_____
_____	_____
_____	_____
_____	_____

■ Circle your favorite word from your lists. Find another person who circled the same words and write ✎ his or her name below.

_____

Purpose: Language Development, Content Skill/Concept Development. Critical/Creative Thinking. *Answers will vary.*

Name _____

A Raindrop's Journey

■ Use what you know about the water cycle to tell the story of "The Adventures of Randy Raindrop."

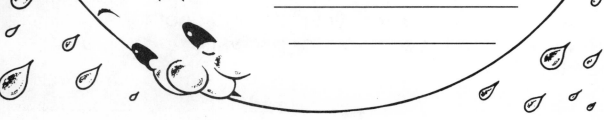

Purpose: Language Development, Content Skill/Concept Development, Critical/Creative Thinking. *Answers will vary.*

Name _____

A Cloudy Week

■ How cloudy is your week? For the next week, record the date and list the cloud formations you see each day.

Cirrus

Cumulus

Stratus

Fog

	Date	Cloud Formations
Monday	_____	_____
Tuesday	_____	_____
Wednesday	_____	_____
Thursday	_____	_____
Friday	_____	_____
Saturday	_____	_____
Sunday	_____	_____

■ Look at your completed list. Which cloud formation did you see most often?

_____

Purpose: Language Development. Content Skill/Concept Development. *Answers will vary.*

Name _____

A Long-Winded Interview

■ The wind blows around the world. Interview the wind by asking the following questions. Write  what you think the wind's answers would be.

Question 1: Where do you come from?

_____

_____

Question 2: Where are you going?

_____

_____

Question 3: Why is it that sometimes you blow very hard and other times you blow softly?

_____

_____

Question 4: Which do you enjoy more, blowing hard or softly? Why?

_____

_____

Question 5: What do you want people to know about you?

_____

_____

Purpose: Language Development, Critical/Creative Thinking. *Answers will vary.*

Name _____

Stormy Questions

■ Write ✏️ a question about
each of the storms below. Then
find someone who can answer
the questions. Write their answers.

Thunderstorm

Question: _____

_____

Answer: _____

_____

Tornado

Question: _____

_____

Answer: _____

_____

Hurricane

Question: _____

_____

Answer: _____

_____

Purpose: Language Development, Content Skill/Concept Development, Critical/Creative Thinking. *Answers will vary.*

Name _____

Two Haiku

■ Write ✎ 2 more haiku. Write
one about a season and the
other about a type of weather.
Remember! 5 - 7 - 5.

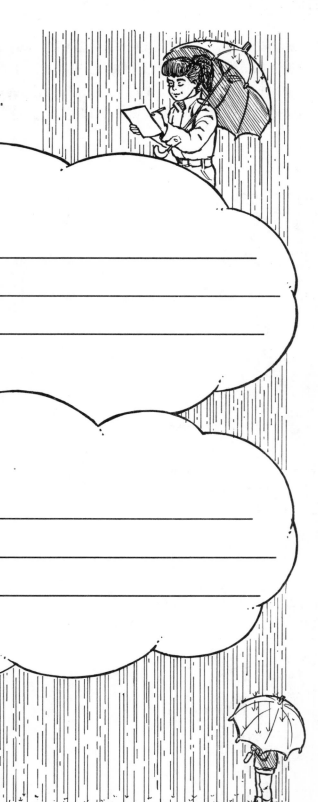

A New System

■ With your partner ✋ , decide
on a new system for organizing
data about space. Give a name
to each category you decide
upon. Then list as many items as
you can for each category.

Category Name:

Category Name:

Category Name:

Category Name:

Purpose: Language Development. Content Skill/Concept Development. *Answers will vary.*

Name _____

Stars on Earth

■ With your partner , list as
many entertainment stars as you
can. Then discuss with your
partner why they are called
"stars." Write 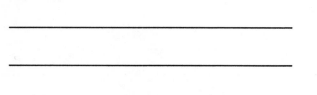 your ideas
below.

1. Stars in the entertainment world:

_____   _____

_____   _____

_____   _____

_____   _____

_____   _____

_____   _____

_____   _____

2. Why they are called "stars":

_____

_____

_____

_____

_____

Purpose: Language Development. Content Skill/Concept Development. *Answers will vary.*

Middle Level C

The Ideal Planet

■ Write ✎ a description of the ideal planet. Include ideas about the weather on the planet, which plants and animals would and would not live there, and what life there would be like. Use the name of your planet in the title.

The Planet of _____

_____

_____

_____

_____

_____

_____

_____

_____

_____

_____

_____

_____

Purpose: Critical/Creative Thinking. *Answers will vary.*

Name _____

Compare the Planets

■ Use Focus Sheet 10.3 to write the diameters of the planets below. Write > (is larger than) or < (is smaller than) to show how they compare.

Mercury		Venus	Earth		Venus
_____	☐	_____	_____	☐	_____

Mercury		Pluto	Neptune		Uranus
_____	☐	_____	_____	☐	_____

Earth		Mars	Jupiter		Saturn
_____	☐	_____	_____	☐	_____

Jupiter		Mars	Uranus		Saturn
_____	☐	_____	_____	☐	_____

Neptune		Pluto	Venus		Pluto
_____	☐	_____	_____	☐	_____

Jupiter		Earth	Saturn		Mars
_____	☐	_____	_____	☐	_____

Pluto		Uranus	Neptune		Jupiter
_____	☐	_____	_____	☐	_____

Saturn		Venus	Mercury		Mars
_____	☐	_____	_____	☐	_____

Purpose: Content Skill/Concept Development.

Middle Level C

Astronaut Supplies

■ Draw  a selection of items you think would be offered in a store for astronauts.

Purpose: Critical/Creative Thinking. *Answers will vary.*

Name _____

Animals in the Space Age

■ How do you think life might be
different for animals in the future?
Write ✏ or draw ✏ your
ideas for each category below.

Food

Transportation

Shelter

Recreation

Powerful Sentences

■ Use the words below to write ✎ a sentence about each god or goddess.

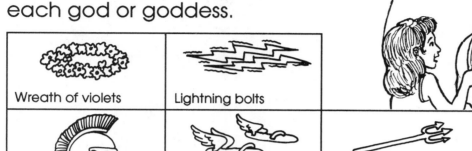

Wreath of violets	Lightning bolts
Helmet	Sandals with wings	Spear with 3 points	Shield

 Jupiter: _____

_____

 Mars: _____

_____

 Mercury: _____

_____

 Venus: _____

_____

 Pluto: _____

_____

 Neptune: _____

_____

Purpose: Language Development. Content Skill/Concept Development. Critical/Creative Thinking. *Answers will vary.*

Name _____

Advice for Phaeton

■ Phaeton has just told you that he is going to drive the chariot of the sun across the sky. Write the advice you would give to Phaeton. You may include personal experiences to support your advice.

_____

_____

_____

_____

_____

_____

_____

_____

_____

_____

_____

_____

Purpose: Content Skill/Concept Development. Critical/Creative Thinking. *Answers will vary.*

Middle Level C

Sunrise ... Sunset

■ With your partner , write definitions for sunrise and sunset. Then answer the questions. You may refer to a dictionary or encyclopedia if you wish.

Sunrise: _____

 _____

_____

_____

Sunset: _____

 _____

_____

_____

1. Does the sun move around the earth or _____ does the earth move around the sun?

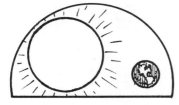 _____

_____

_____

2. What causes sunrise and sunset. _____

 _____

_____

Purpose: Language Development. Content Skill/Concept Development. *Answers will vary.*

An Eyewitness Report

■ You were with Proserpina when she was kidnapped. Write  your eyewitness account of what happened. Include a description of the kidnapper and tell what you did.

1. What happened? _____

_____

_____

_____

_____

_____

_____

2. What did the kidnapper look like? _____

_____

_____

3. What did <u>you</u> do? _____

_____

_____

Purpose: Content Skill/Concept Development. Critical/Creative Thinking. **Answers will vary.**

● Name _____

My Favorite Character

■ Which character from "The Myth of Proserpina" is your favorite? Write  the character's name and 3 reasons why he or she is your favorite.

Proserpina   Ceres   Jupiter   Mercury   Pluto

My favorite character is _____

Reasons why this character is my favorite:

1. _____

   _____

   _____

2. _____

   _____

   _____

3. _____

   _____

   _____

● ■ Find another person who chose the same character. Write  the person's name:

_____

Purpose: Language Development, Content Skill/Concept Development, Critical/Creative Thinking. *Answers will vary.*

Name _____

Uncommon Comparisons

■ With your partner 🤝, list ways that gods/goddesses and humans are alike and ways they are different.

Gods and
Goddesses

Alike —

Humans

Purpose: Language Development, Content Skill/Concept Development, Critical/Creative Thinking. **Answers will vary.**

Just One Thing ...

■ You have given up life in the city and now enjoy living in the mountains. You are able to meet your basic needs but you have no luxuries. You have decided to add one nonessential item—something that you do not <u>need</u> but would like to have. Write ✎ a paragraph describing what you will choose and how it will affect your lifestyle.

Purpose: Content Skill/Concept Development. Critical/Creative Thinking. *Answers will vary.*

_____

_____

_____

_____

_____

_____

_____

_____

_____

_____

_____

Name _____

Future Survival

■ Predict how people will meet the basic needs of food, shelter, and clothing 100 years from now. Write  and/or draw what they may look like.

Food

_____

Shelter

_____

Clothing

_____

Dear Diary ...

■ You are living with your parents on the frontier in the year 1800. Write  a diary entry describing what you did today. Include your chores and any other family responsibilities.

Purpose: Content Skill/Concept Development. Critical/Creative Thinking. *Answers will vary.*

Television Values

■ With your partner  , decide on a favorite television program. Write ✐ its name and list 3 values that you think are represented in the program. Then decide if each value is positive (+) or negative (-). Write the correct word on the line.

Purpose: Language Development. Content Skill/Concept Development. Critical/Creative Thinking. **Answers will vary.**

Name of Television Program

_____

Three Values in the Program

1. _____

_____

Positive or Negative: _____

2. _____

_____

Positive or Negative: _____

3. _____

_____

Positive or Negative: _____

Monthly Celebrations

■ With your partner , find a holiday (or the birthday of a famous person) for each month of the year. Write ✎ the name of the holiday (or birthday person) and the date for each month.

Month	Name of Holiday or Birthday Person	Date
January	_____	_____
February	_____	_____
March	_____	_____
April	_____	_____
May	_____	_____
June	_____	_____
July	_____	_____
August	_____	_____
September	_____	_____
October	_____	_____
November	_____	_____
December	_____	_____

■ Which special day is you favorite?

_____

Purpose: Language Development, Content Skill/Concept Development. *Answers will vary.*

Symbolic Questions

■ Write ✐ a question about
each of the symbols below.
Then find someone who can
answer your questions. Write
their responses. (If you can't
find anyone who knows the
answers look them up in the
encyclopedia.)

**American
eagle**

Question: _____

_____

Answer: _____

_____

**American
flag**

Question: _____

_____

Answer: _____

_____

**Statue
of Liberty**

Question: _____

_____

Answer: _____

_____

Middle Level C
Focus Sheets

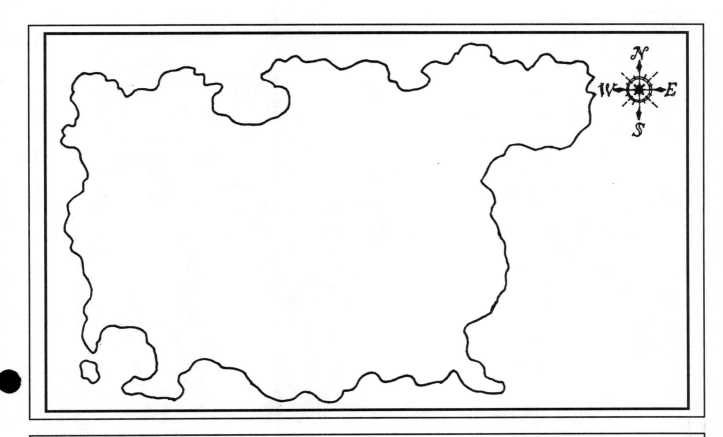

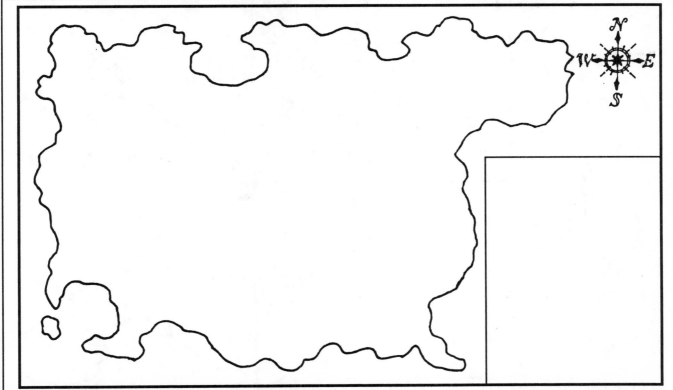

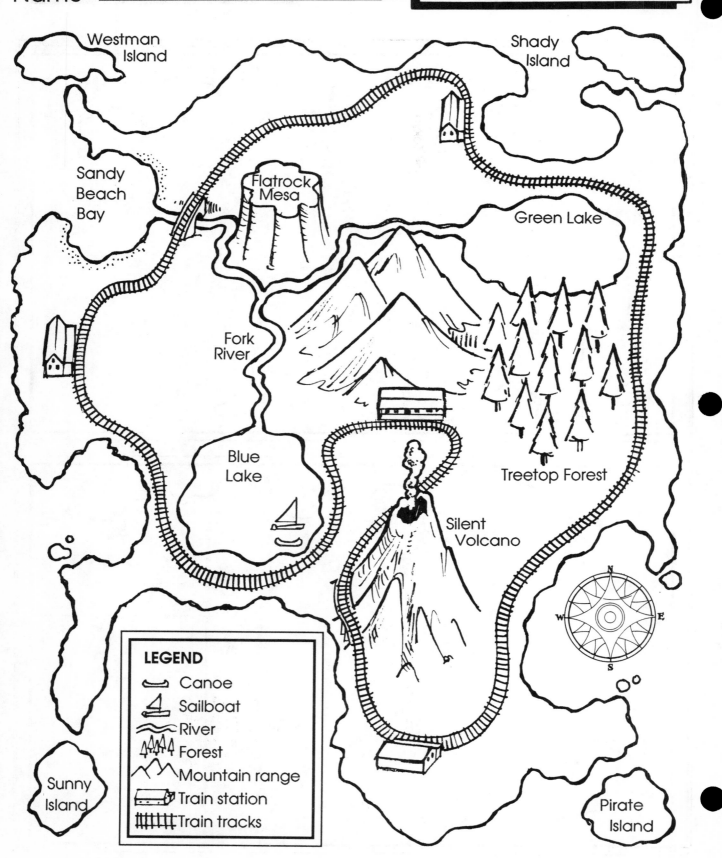

Name _____

 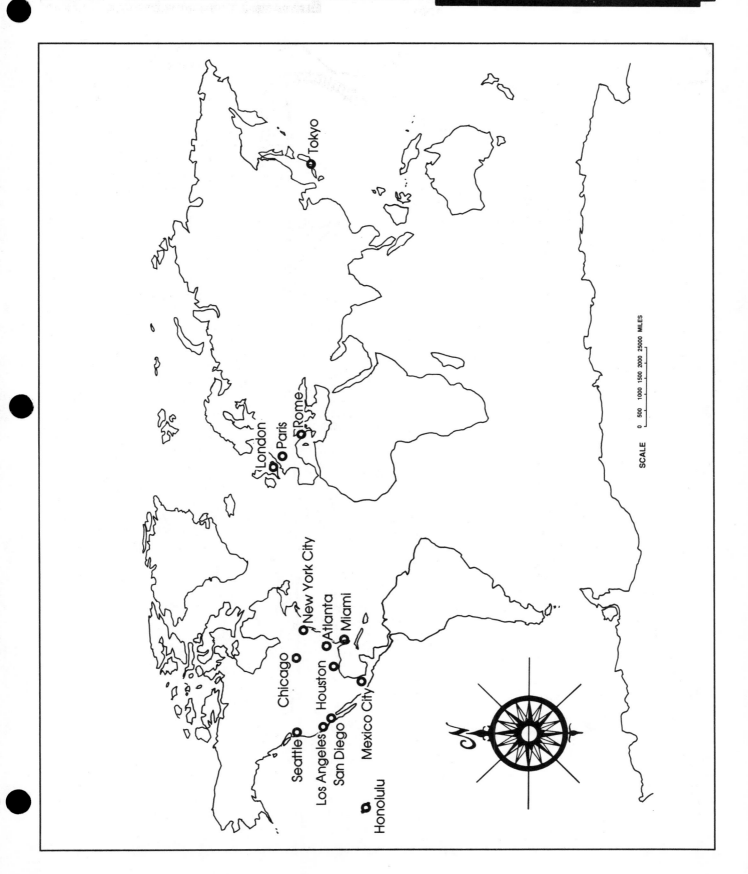

Name _____

Political Map

_____

_____

_____

Physical Map

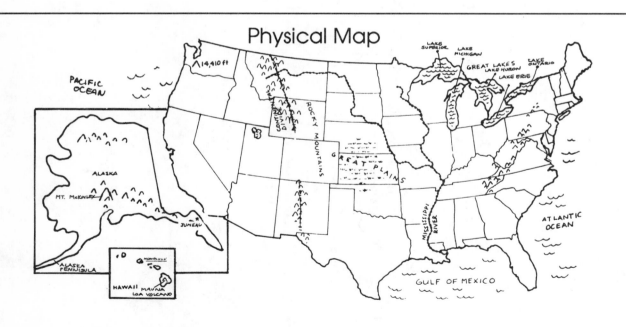

_____

_____

_____

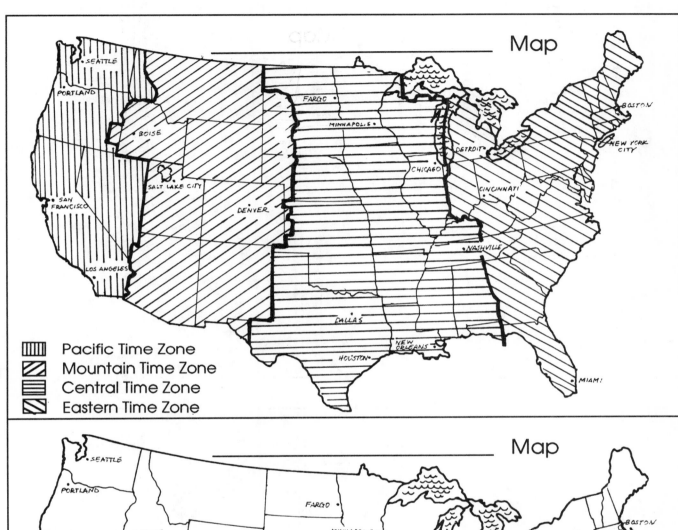

_____ Map

Legend:
- ▮▮▮ Pacific Time Zone
- ⧄⧄⧄ Mountain Time Zone
- ▤▤▤ Central Time Zone
- ⧅⧅⧅ Eastern Time Zone

_____ Map

Name _____

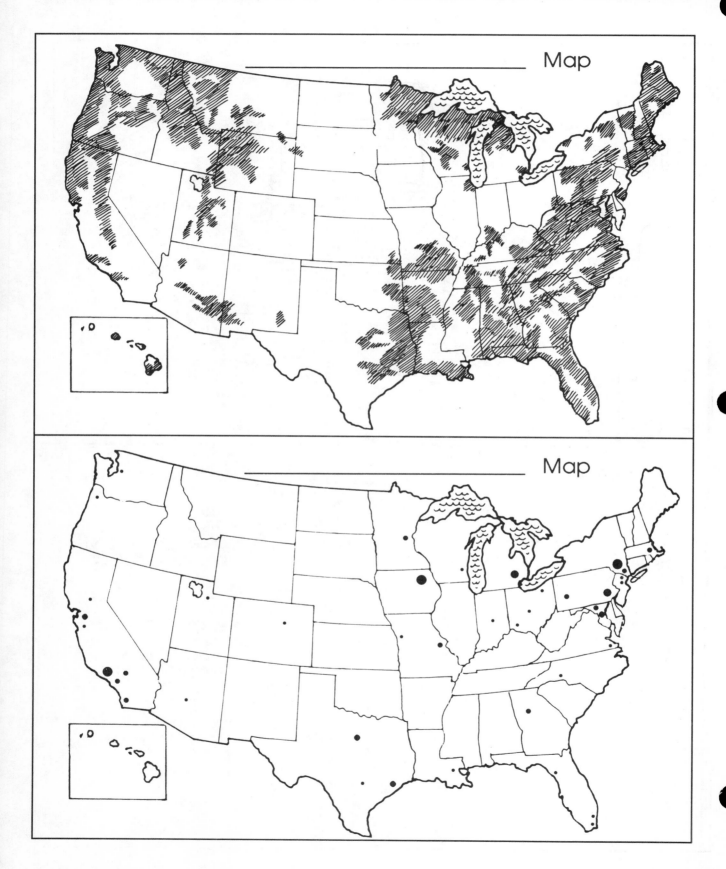

Map _____

Map _____

Leif Ericson

Christopher Columbus

Vasco de Gama

Vasco Nuñez de Balboa

Juan Ponce de Leon

Ferdinand Magellan

YURI GAGARIN

ALAN SHEPHARD

JOHN GLENN

EDWIN ALDRIN

MICHAEL COLLINS

NEIL ARMSTRONG

HERE MEN FROM THE PLANET EARTH
FIRST SET FOOT UPON THE MOON
JULY 1969 A.D.
WE CAME IN PEACE FOR ALL MANKIND

ROBERT CRIPPEN

SALLY RIDE

JOHN YOUNG

Paul Bunyan was the greatest logger in North America. It is said that he was taller than a tree and could chop down an entire forest in one day. His ax was as wide as a barn door. Its handle was a giant oak tree. He could run faster than the fastest deer and cross a river with one step!

Once, Paul started bouncing up and down in the cradle. He bounced so hard he caused a huge tidal wave that flooded the coast of Maine. After that, Paul's parents moved inland to keep Paul out of trouble.

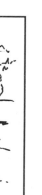

Folks say that when Paul Bunyan was born he was so large it took 14 cows to provide enough milk for him. Paul's father built him a huge cradle that floated in a harbor along the coast of Maine. The ocean waves would rock him to sleep.

2

As Paul grew up, he helped his father to do the farm work. Paul was very strong. Once he was plowing a field with two oxen. When he came to the end of a row, he found he didn't have enough room to turn around. So he just picked up the oxen and the plow and turned them around to start a new row.

4

Even though Paul was very large, he was as quick as lightning. It is said that when he blew out his candle at night, he could jump into bed before the room was dark.

5

Babe and Paul were the best of friends. Babe grew so fast that one day Paul found him grazing in a field with the barn on his back. He had grown right out of the barn overnight! Every day Babe would eat a ton of hay and three wagonloads of turnips for dessert. Whenever Babe was good, Paul would give him an 80 pound lump of sugar. But Babe was so full of mischief, he didn't always get the sugar!

7

One winter day, snow began to fall. But it was very strange snow. It wasn't white – it was a soft blue color. As he was walking home, Paul saw two ears sticking up through the snow. He pulled on the ears, and a baby ox came out of the snow. The ox was cold and hungry. Paul decided to take him home and keep him for a pet. He named the ox Babe. The strangest thing about Babe was that his coat remained blue. The Winter of the Blue Snow had colored him forever.

6

One day Paul Bunyan left home to start his own lumber camp. He hired the best loggers he could find to work with him. Some of them cut paths through the woods, others cut down the trees, and another group sawed trees into logs. Then Babe, the blue ox, would pull the logs down to the river, where they could be floated to the sawmill.

8

One of the most important parts of the lumber camp was the kitchen. The camp had over 200 cooks. Hot Biscuit Slim was the head cook. To make soup, he would row out into the middle of a huge kettle with boatloads of vegetables and shovel them into the water for cooking.

9

At mealtime, the table was crowded with helpers rushing around on roller skates and bicycles. It was the only way they could keep food on the table and drinking glasses filled. Mealtime was very important at Paul Bunyan's lumber camp.

11

To make pancakes, Slim strapped slabs of bacon on the feet of his kitchen
helpers. The helpers then skated around a huge griddle until it was well
greased. The pancakes made on the griddle were so large that it took five
men to eat one. Except for Paul, of course. He would eat 12 or 14 pancakes
every day.

10

Paul Bunyan, Babe, and the workers at the lumber camp had many exciting
adventures together. But one hot, dry autumn, a fire burned all the trees in the
forest. There was no more work, and the loggers went to work for other lumber
camps. Paul and Babe set out to find another forest, and no one has seen
them since.

But some loggers of today will tell you that the sound of the wind blowing
through the trees is actually Paul Bunyan walking through the forests with Babe,
as he did many, many years ago.

12

Name _____

Joe Magarac, Mystery Man of Steel

THUMP! THUMP! THUMP! The houses along Bessemer Street began to shake. Windows rattled and leaves fell off the trees. But Pete and his wife, Mary, weren't worried at all. It was their friend Joe Magarac, on his way to work at the steel mill.

Joe was a giant of a man, 20 feet tall. As he passed Pete's house, he swung his friend onto his shoulders as easily as if Pete were a rag doll. Then off to work they went.

Other people on Bessemer Street often asked Mary questions about Joe. "Where do you think a man like that came from?" they asked. "Some say he was found in a mine, deep in the center of the earth. Others say he came from a faraway star, maybe from another galaxy."

But Mary thought she knew. "Pete says Joe is a man, just bigger and stronger than most. But I remember seeing a comet last winter. It made a bright streak across the sky. And the very next day, Joe was seen in town for the first time."

Joe and Pete arrived at the mill ready for work. Joe took his place at the biggest furnace of all. He looked around to make sure no one was watching but Pete. Then he stuck his entire arm into the vat of molten steel and stirred it. As he stirred, he sang a song, "I really love my work, and I'm happiest when I'm making steel."

Next, Joe grabbed a handful of molten steel and squeezed out yard after yard of railroad track. He laughed as he rolled another handful around his little finger to make dozens of train wheels. Then he stretched some more steel to make supports for buildings. Soon the mill yard was full of steel.

Joe said, "I can make more steel in a day than 20 men can make in a month!" Unfortunately, he was about to learn that he had made too much.

After work, the boss called the workers together. He told them, "We must close the mill for a few days. There is no more iron to make steel, and we can't buy more until we sell all the railroad tracks and wheels we have already made. Our biggest buyer needs steel right away. If we can't fill his order in 2 days, he will buy from another steel mill."

Joe was very worried. He knew Pete and the other workers had wives and families, and the loss of even one day's pay would be hard on them. Joe thought, "What can I do to help my friends?"

2

Middle Level C

That evening the workers met at Pete's house to talk about the closing of the steel mill. Someone asked, "Where is Joe? He could give us some ideas about what to do."

Pete went outside to see if Joe was coming. What he saw instead made him call to the other workers, "Look, there are orange and yellow lights all over the sky!" Everyone looked at the lights. They seemed to be coming from the steel mill.

By now, others had noticed the lights too. Soon many people were racing toward the mill. They shouted, "The mill is on fire!"

When they reached the mill, they found a huge fire in the largest furnace – Joe's furnace. Everyone but Pete ran to check the other furnaces. Pete ran to Joe's furnace. He thought he heard a voice singing.

Pete climbed to a high platform and looked down into the vat of molten steel, as hot and bright as the sun. In the vat, up to his waist in steel, was Joe Magarac, singing happily.

Pete called to Joe, "Jump out of there. The steel will burn you!"

Joe laughed. "Burn me? This steel is me. I'm just doing something I've dreamed about doing all my life. I'm turning into the finest steel! The steel I am making will save the mill and all your jobs!"

By the time the men climbed up to the platform, all they could see was beautiful, molten steel. Later, when the workers poured the steel, it shone like the tail of a big, fiery comet. It was the finest steel anyone had ever seen. The steel was made into all the things the mill's biggest customer had ordered, and many other things too.

The fine steel saved the mill. And no one but Pete knew where it came from. That steel, like the legend of Joe Magarac, has lasted from that day to this.

Middle Level C

Paul Bunyan   Same   Joe Magarac

_____

_____

_____

_____

_____

_____

_____

_____

_____

_____

_____

Willing Immigrants

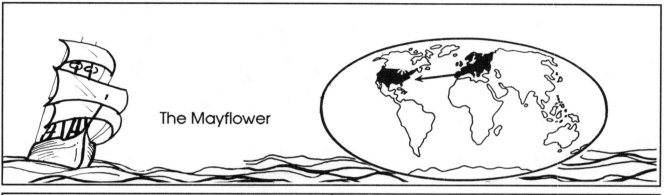

Unwilling Immigrants

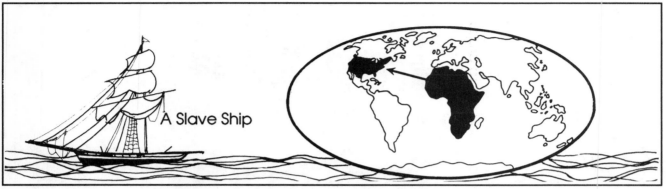

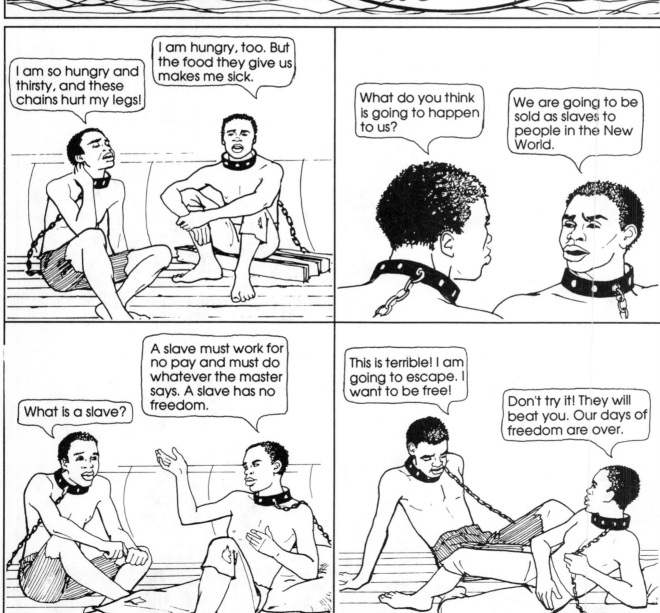

The Irish

In the 1800s, potatoes were the main food for many people in Ireland. Then, the potato crops failed and many people starved. During the famine years, 1 1/2 million Irish sailed to America. These immigrants were very poor. Although most had been farmers in Ireland, they could not afford to buy land in America. Many lived in poor housing areas in the large cities. They worked on the railroads, in mines, and in factories. Others worked as laborers or servants.

Many people in America, especially in the cities, did not like the Irish. Even when they needed workers, many stores and factories would not hire the Irish. It was common to see signs that read, "No Irish need apply."

Over time, the Irish became more accepted. The children of immigrants went to school, and as adults made contributions in many areas. They became fire fighters, police officers, teachers, and politicians—among many other professions. And in 1960, John F. Kennedy, the great-grandson of an Irish immigrant, became the President of the United States.

Chinese Immigrants

The Chinese were the first large group of immigrants to come to America from Asia. There was a great famine in China in the mid-1800s. There wasn't enough food, and people were starving. But they heard that in California, there were lots of jobs with good pay.

When the Chinese arrived in America, some found jobs as gardeners or cooks; others worked in laundries. Even though they worked very hard, the Chinese were paid less money than other workers.

Life was difficult for the Chinese. Many people misunderstood them because their clothes, customs, and language were different. Some people were afraid the Chinese would take away their jobs. At one time there were even laws that stopped the Chinese from coming to America and would not allow anyone born in China to become a citizen of the United States. In time, however, those laws were changed. Despite their hardships, the Chinese immigrants made great contributions, especially in farming and business.

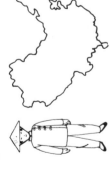

Name _____

_____
_____

_____
_____

_____
_____

_____
_____

Harriet Beecher Stowe was born on June 14, 1811.

While living in Connecticut, Harriet met slaves who had escaped from the South. From them, she learned about the difficulties they endured on the plantations.

Harriet wrote a book called *Uncle Tom's Cabin*. It was the story of a plantation slave who was owned by one man, sold to another and then sold twice again. Her story was so popular that newspapers reprinted it, as a weekly series.

Her book made many people in the North realize that slavery violated basic human rights – the rights to freedom and fair treatment.

Uncle Tom was a loyal slave who was owned by a kind master. But the master, Mr. Shelby, had to sell Tom because he needed money to pay his debts.

Uncle Tom's new owner was a kind man, too. But when the owner died, Uncle Tom was sold to a man named Simon Legree, who treated his slaves cruelly.

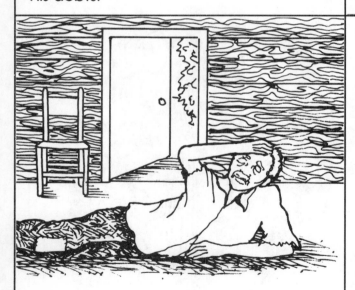

Simon Legree often beat his slaves until they fell to the ground. Uncle Tom never fought back, and soon he became very ill from the beatings.

Mr. Shelby finally found Uncle Tom and bought him back from Simon Legree. But by then, Uncle Tom was very sick and weak. When he died, Mr. Shelby buried him in a peaceful spot. After that, Mr. Shelby decided that it was not right to keep slaves, and he gave all his own slaves their freedom.

Harriet Tubman

Harriet Tubman was born into slavery in about 1820 in Dorchester County, Maryland. In 1849, she escaped the plantation. Harriet made her way to the northern states by way of the Underground Railroad, the route slaves used to escape by traveling during safe times and hiding in certain safe places.

After obtaining her freedom, Harriet returned to the South to guide members of her family north. Later she continued to lead hundreds of slaves through the Underground Railroad to freedom in the North.

In the North, Harriet became a leading activist in the fight to abolish slavery before the Civil War. Later, during the war, she joined the forces of the Union and worked as a nurse, laundress, and even spy to help ensure that slavery would end.

Susan B. Anthony

When Susan B. Anthony was born, in 1820, women's employment and education opportunities were limited. All their earnings and possessions legally belonged to their husbands. Fortunately for Susan, she was able to go to college and obtain a teaching job, although the pay for female teachers was much lower than for male teachers.

After teaching for 15 years, Susan became involved in the important reform movements of the times. She fought for women to be able to keep the money that they earned for themselves, for women's right to vote, and for equal pay.

She spent 33 years fighting for women's rights and suffrage. When she died in 1906, women had gained the right to keep their own earnings and possessions, but they still had not achieved the right to vote.

When Helen was 19 months old, she came down with a mysterious illness that caused a very high fever. Although her family was relieved when her temperature returned to normal, they soon realized that Helen could no longer see or hear.

3

Helen Keller was born on June 27, 1880, in Tuscumbia, Alabama. She was a happy, lively child, and her parents thought she was extremely bright.

2

Helen's cheerful personality disappeared, and she became frustrated and angry. Because she could not hear, she soon forgot how to talk. Now she communicated only with cries and grunts.

4

After a while, Helen developed her own set of signs and signals to express herself. Cutting and buttering motions meant she wanted bread and butter, pretending to put on eyeglasses meant "Father," and pulling her hair to the back of her head meant "Mother." But she grew more and more frustrated and angry that she could not speak.

5

Mr. Bell recommended that Anne Mansfield Sullivan become Helen's teacher. Miss Sullivan had once been blind, but after many operations had regained her sight. Even though she had no experience in teaching, Anne Sullivan was determined to succeed in her new job.

7

Helen's parents spent several years trying to find someone to help educate her. Finally, when she was 6 years old, they appealed to Alexander Graham Bell for help. Better known today as the inventor of the telephone, Bell was originally a teacher of the deaf and founded a school for them.

6

Miss Sullivan tried to teach Helen the names of objects by tracing the alphabet spelling of the words onto her palm. One day, as Helen held one hand under the water running from a pump, Miss Sullivan spelled "water" over and over again into her other hand. Suddenly, Helen understood, and from that moment she was eager to learn everything in her new language.

8

Helen now referred to Anne Sullivan as "Teacher." And Teacher taught Helen to read and write in Braille, a system of raised dots that represent letters.

9

With the help and support of her dear Teacher, Helen was able to attend and graduate from Radcliffe College. Anne Sullivan had spelled out all of the lectures for every class into Helen's hand.

11

Later, Helen learned to speak by feeling the position of Teacher's mouth and touching her throat to feel the vibrations as Teacher spoke. After 10 lessons, Helen said her first sentence. Although most people could not understand her and an interpreter was always necessary when she spoke, Helen continued to practice and use her voice.

10

Helen devoted her life to aiding the blind and the deaf. She wrote books and gave lectures to improve the public's knowledge, awareness, and understanding of the needs of people whose sight or hearing were impaired. Helen Keller was recognized by many organizations, even by nations outside the United States, for her outstanding humanitarian contributions. And now, long after her death in 1968, at age 87, she is still remembered and admired.

12

Name _____

We the People of the United States, _____

_____

_____

in order to form a more perfect union, _____

_____

_____

establish justice, _____

_____

insure domestic tranquillity, _____

_____

provide for the common defense, _____

_____

_____

promote the general welfare, _____

_____

and secure the blessings of liberty to ourselves and our posterity,

_____

_____

do ordain and establish this Constitution for the United States of
America. _____

_____

Five more amendments: 13,15, 16, 19, and 25

Opinion

 Order: _____	**Income tax:** This amendment gave Congress the power to collect tax on incomes, the money that people earn. It was amendment number _____ , added in the year _____ .
 Order: _____	**All men given right to vote:** No citizen can be kept from voting because of race or skin color. This was amendment number _____ , added in the year _____ .
 Order: _____	**Slavery abolished:** This amendment ended slavery in the United States. It was amendment number _____ , added in the year _____ .
 Order: _____	**Women given right to vote:** Until this amendment was passed, women were not allowed to vote. It was amendment number _____ , passed in the year _____ .
 Order: _____	**Vice-president becomes acting president:** When the president of the United States dies or can no longer do the job, the vice-president takes over the duties of the president. This was amendment _____ , passed in the year _____ .

Middle Level C

House of Representatives   Senate

Legislative Branch: Congress

	Senate	House of Representatives
How many?	100 (2 from each state)	435 (number from each state based on population; all states have at least 1)
How are they chosen?	Elected by voters of entire state	Elected by voters in specific geographic areas (districts) of state
Term of office	6 years	2 years
Age requirement	30 years	25 years
Citizenship	U.S. citizen for at least 9 years	U.S. citizen for at least 7 years
Who leads them?	Vice-president of U.S. serves as president of Senate, but doesn't vote except to break a tie	Members select a Speaker of the House

Name _____

Executive Branch

Judicial Branch

	Executive Branch	Judicial Branch
How many?	1 president, 1 vice-president	9 justices (judges)
How are they chosen?	Elected by voters from entire U.S.	Selected by the president; must be approved by the Senate
Term of office	4 years	Appointed for life
Age requirement	35 years	None specified
Citizenship requirement	Born in United States	None specified
Who leads them?	President	Chief Justice

Middle Level C

Ask Dr. Discover

Dear Dr. Discover,

Something terrible has happened to me!
My mom says that if I don't organize my
room she won't let me watch TV! I don't
understand what's wrong with my room.
I always clean it up by pushing all my toys
and clothes and books and shoes and
homework and trash under the bed.

What does she mean by "organize,"
anyway?

Sincerely,

Messy Mervin

Dear Messy Mervin,

_____

_____

_____

_____

_____

_____

Sincerely,

_____

Ask Dr. Discover

Dear Dr. Discover,

I am so upset! I simply cannot find my roller skates!

Yesterday my sneaky brother was riding around on a new skateboard that he built himself. The wheels on it look just like the wheels on my roller skates.

Do you think this could be related? If so how?

Sincerely,

Very Suspicious
(not my real name)

Dear Very Suspicious,

_____

_____

_____

_____

_____

_____

Sincerely,

_____

_____

Rhamphorhynchus

Brontosaurus

Triceratops

Trachodon

Ichthyosaurus

Tyrannosaurus rex

1. _____

2. _____

3. _____

4. _____

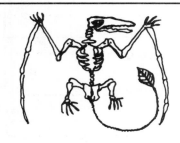

5. _____

6. _____

Questionnaire		Yes 2	Maybe 1	No 0
1. Would you enjoy working outdoors studying rocks and soil?	**C**			
2. Would you enjoy learning about chemicals and ways to use them?	**A**			
3. Would you enjoy helping people stay healthy?	**B**			
4. Would you enjoy studying the planets and the stars?	**C**			
5. Do you enjoy taking things apart to find out how they work?	**A**			
6. Would you enjoy growing plants and studying their many uses?	**B**			
7. Would you like to learn how to predict the weather?	**C**			
8. Are you interested in how electrical power can be produced and used?	**A**			
9. Would you enjoy working with animals and studying their habits?	**B**			
10. Would you like to know more about how the ocean affects out lives?	**C**			
11. Would you like to help find new sources of energy for the future?	**A**			
12. Would you enjoy studying extinct plants and animals?	**B**			

A. Physical science Total points: _____	**B. Life science** Total points: _____	**C. Earth/space science** Total points: _____

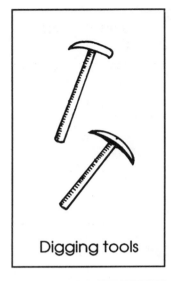

Digging tools

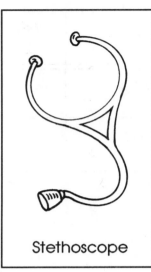

Stethoscope

Test tubes

Scale

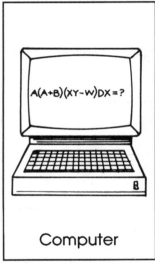

Computer

Drafting table

Magnifying glass

Weather map

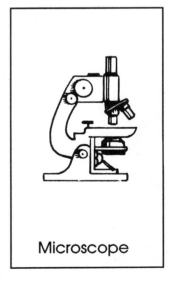

Microscope

Barometer

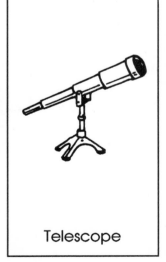

Telescope

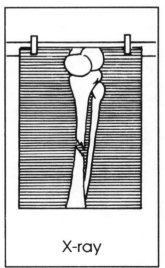

X-ray

Careers in Science

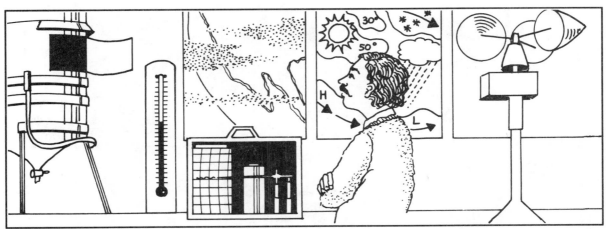

A meteorologist studies the weather and its effects on the environment. Information on wind speed, cloud formations, and storm conditions are important to a meteorologist. Much of this information comes from weather satellites in space.

3

Paleontologists study fossils of plants and animals that lived millions of years ago. Some paleontologists work in museums, where dinosaur bones are put back together for display. Others help find and dig up fossils. Paleontologists work with other scientists to learn all they can about life many years ago.

2

Geologists learn about the history of the earth by studying its rocks and soil. They also study landforms such as mountains, riverbeds, and valleys. Careers related to geology include seismology (the study of earthquakes), volcanology (the study of volcanoes), and gemology (the study of gems).

4

Astronomers use powerful telescopes to observe the stars, the planets and their moons, even entire galaxies. They also study information sent back to earth by satellites in space. Astronomers work with other scientists in related careers, such as mathematicians, who use math to determine how far away planets and stars are from earth.

5

Chemists study liquids, solids, and gases to see what they are made of and how they work. These scientists sometimes carefully mix chemicals to see what will happen. In the laboratory, some chemists use test tubes, microscopes, and other tools to help discover new medicines. Other chemists create new materials for a variety of uses.

7

Aeronautical engineers design aircraft and spacecraft. They must have excellent math skills so that they can design planes and spaceships that will be strong enough to withstand the forces of flight. These science professionals draw plans for their new designs on paper and test them with computers before the planes or spacecraft are built. The people who actually build the vehicles follow the plans of the aeronautical engineers.

6

Biologists are science professionals who study plant and animal life. Many biologists study forms of life so tiny that they can be seen only with a microscope, such as the bacteria that make people sick. When biologists study bacteria, they experiment to learn how the bacteria grow and what causes them to die.

8

Plant or Animal?

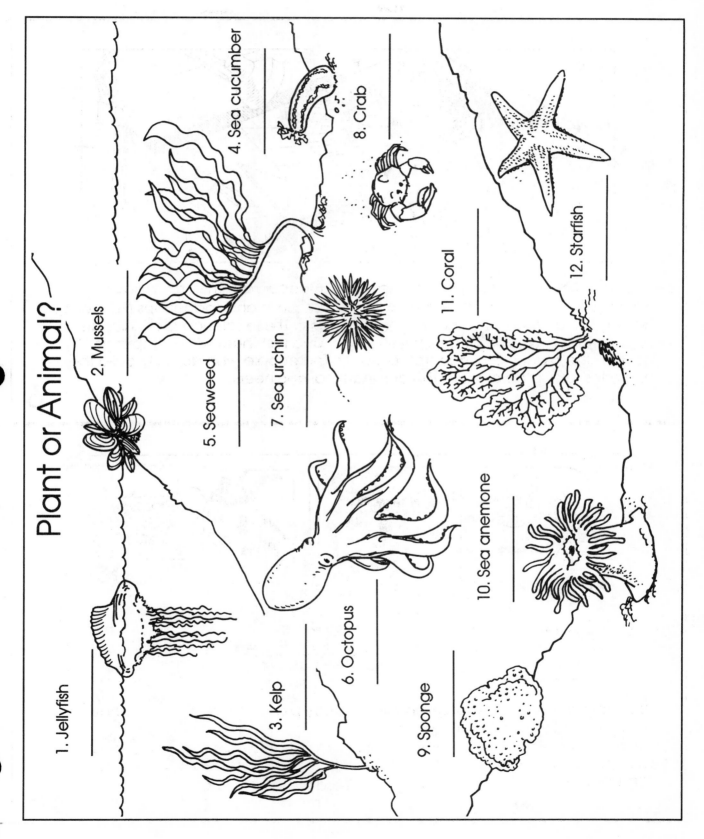

1. Jellyfish _____

2. Mussels _____

3. Kelp _____

4. Sea cucumber _____

5. Seaweed _____

6. Octopus _____

7. Sea urchin _____

8. Crab _____

9. Sponge _____

10. Sea anemone _____

11. Coral _____

12. Starfish _____

Name _____

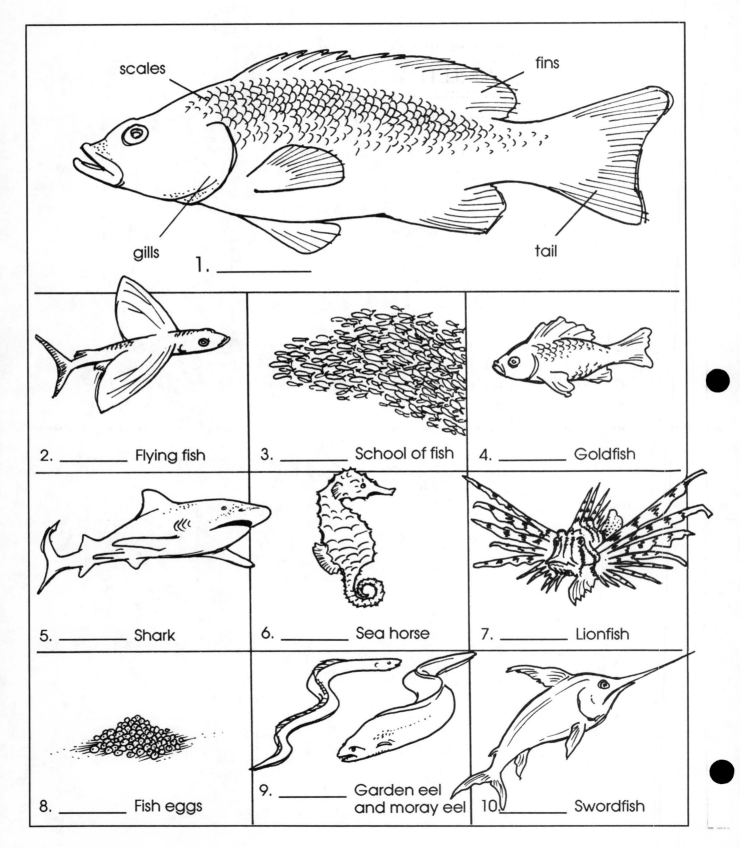

scales

fins

gills

tail

1. _____

2. _____ Flying fish

3. _____ School of fish

4. _____ Goldfish

5. _____ Shark

6. _____ Sea horse

7. _____ Lionfish

8. _____ Fish eggs

9. _____ Garden eel and moray eel

10. _____ Swordfish

Name _____

Marine Mammals

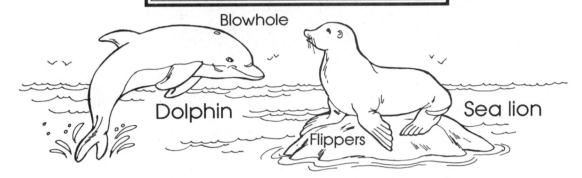

Blowhole

Dolphin

Flippers

Sea lion

Marine mammals live in and near the ocean. Dolphins and other whales that live in the ocean may look like fish, but they are not. They breathe air through a hole in the top of their heads, called a blowhole, and move their tails up and down when they swim. (Fish move their tails from side to side.) Other marine mammals, like the sea lion, spend most of their time in the ocean, using their flippers to swim, but they often rest on rocks and beaches.

Baleen Whales

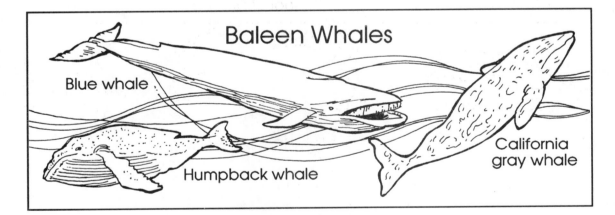

Blue whale

Humpback whale

California gray whale

Baleen whales are enormous marine mammals, but they feed on microscopic organisms known as plankton. These whales trap the plankton in their baleen, the curtainlike filter (or strainer) in their mouth. There are many kinds of baleen whales. They all have blowholes. One of them, the blue whale, is the largest animal on earth and weighs more than 30 elephants! The California gray whale migrates along the West Coast each year. And the gentle, grayish Humpback whale can often be heard "singing."

3

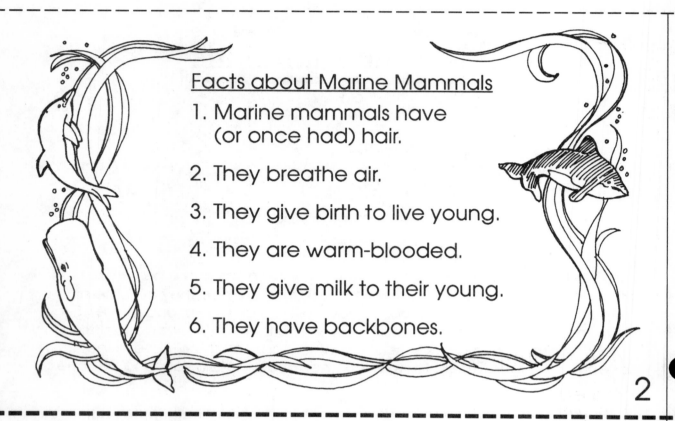

Facts about Marine Mammals

1. Marine mammals have (or once had) hair.

2. They breathe air.

3. They give birth to live young.

4. They are warm-blooded.

5. They give milk to their young.

6. They have backbones.

2

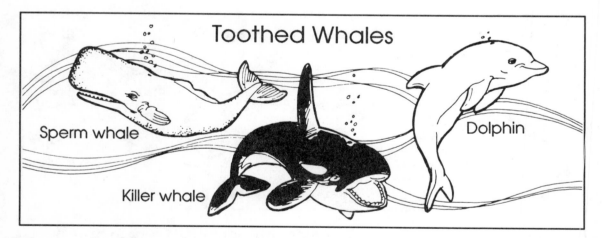

Toothed Whales

Sperm whale

Killer whale

Dolphin

There are about 72 kinds of toothed whales. They all have teeth for eating fish, and a blowhole. And toothed whales also have very good hearing. The brown sperm whale, the largest toothed whale, can dive almost 4,000 feet deep and stay under water for 90 minutes! The dolphin is gray and small, but very fast and very smart! The black-and-white killer whale, a very good hunter, eats other marine mammals as well as fish.

4

Walrus

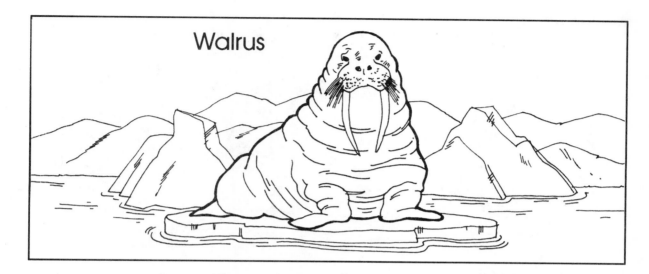

The walrus lives in cold Arctic waters. A thick layer of fat, called blubber, helps this large mammal stay warm. It has light brown skin and thick whiskers, which help in locating food. They eat clam, snails, and other sea animals that live on the ocean floor. The male walrus has 2 long tusks.

5

Sea Lion

Sea lions are brown. They use their paddle-shaped flippers like arms and legs. They can sit on and move their back flippers. They swim by moving their flippers like wings. Sea lions are good divers and can stay under water for 10 to 20 minutes. They use their eyes, ears, and whiskers to find their way through the water. Sea lions spend much of their time on land.

7

Sea Otters

The playful sea otter lives in the icy water of Alaska and along the California coast. Sometimes an otter will lie on its back, place a rock on its chest, and smash a clam or other shellfish against the rock to break it open to eat. This marine mammal has thick brown fur and eats sea urchins, abalone, and other small sea animals.

6

Harbor Seal

Harbor seals are very clumsy on land. Unlike sea lions, which they closely resemble, seals cannot bend their back flippers under their bodies to help them move. But they are very good swimmers. They can dive to about 1,000 feet and stay under water for 30 minutes. Adult harbor seals are brown with big brown eyes.

8

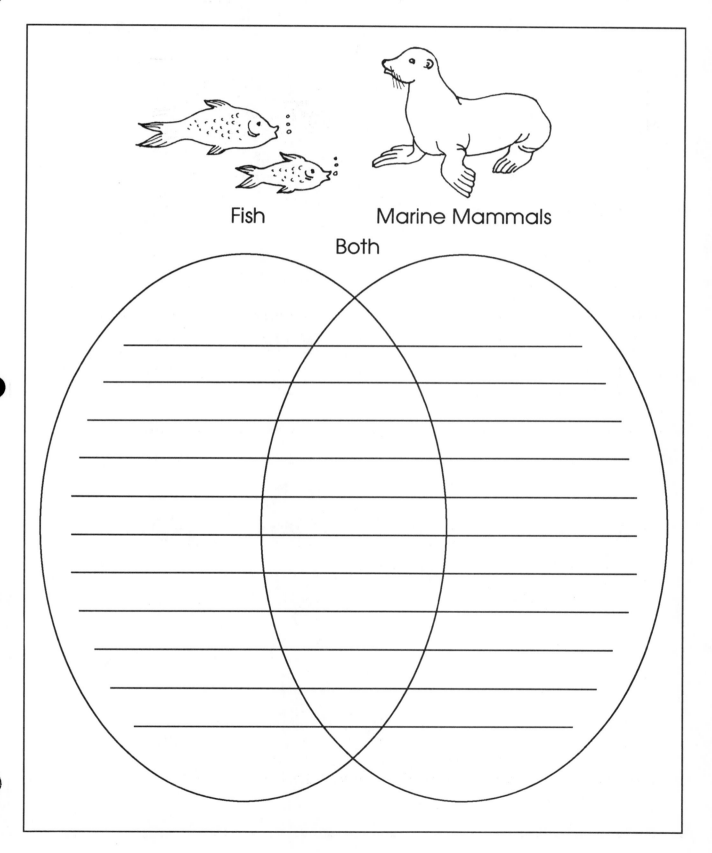

Fish

Marine Mammals

Both

The Water Cycle

Precipitation

Condensation

Evaporation

Name _____

Precipitation

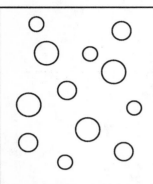

Rain: Rain is water falling from clouds. Drops of water inside a cloud are always moving. Tiny drops bump into one another, stick together, and grow bigger. When they get so big and heavy that the cloud can't hold them – and if the air is not too cold – the drops fall to earth as rain.

Raindrops are perfectly round!

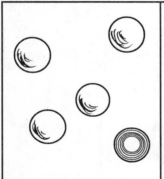

Hail: Hailstones are formed when raindrops are blown upward into a very cold cloud and freeze. Air currents keep the icy hailstones moving up and down inside the cloud or in the air. Each time the hailstones go up and down, they get a little bigger because more raindrops stick to them and freeze.

Count the layers to see how many times this hailstone bounced up and down inside a cloud before it fell to earth.

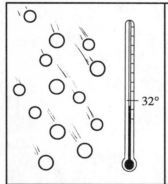

32°

Sleet: Sleet begins as rain. When the air is very cold, drops of water freeze before they reach the ground. The raindrops turn into tiny balls of ice.

Sleet is frozen rain.

Snow: Snowflakes are formed inside clouds that float through freezing-cold air. The water in these clouds freezes, forming tiny ice crystals instead of becoming raindrops. As the air gets colder, more water condenses around the ice and the crystals grow larger. These ice crystals always have 6 sides, no matter how big they are. Usually, 2 or more crystals stick together. When they are too large to float in the air, they fall to earth as snow.

Clouds

- High altitude (above 20,000 feet)
- Feathery appearance

_____

- Middle altitude (6,500 to 20,000 feet)
- Big, fluffy
- Fair weather

_____

- Low altitude (below 6,500 feet)
- Flat, layered
- Indicate changing weather; may bring rain

_____

- Very low; close to or touching the ground
- Cool, damp

_____

Name _____

Wind

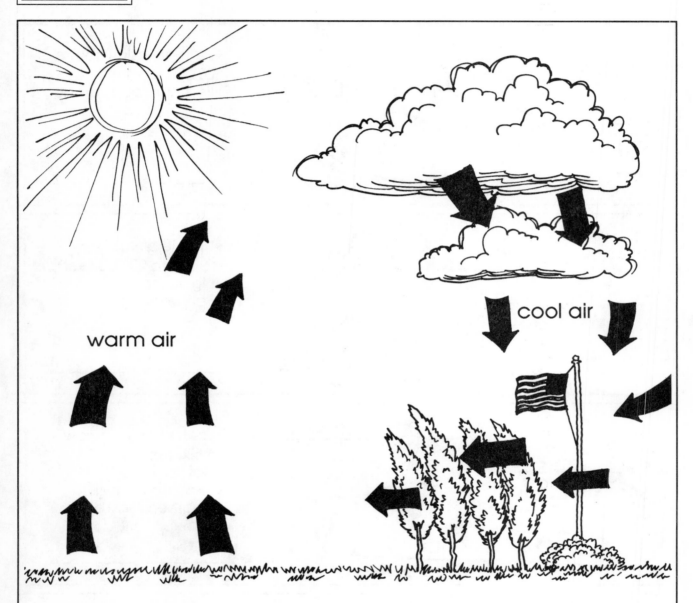

warm air

cool air

Wind is moving air. Air always moves from cool areas to warm areas. When the sun warms the earth, it also warms the air near the ground. As the air gets warmer, it begins to rise, and cool air moves in to take its place. This movement of air is what we feel as wind.

Also, as the warm air moves upward, it becomes cooler. It will then return to earth to repeat the cycle.

Middle Level C

Thunderstorm

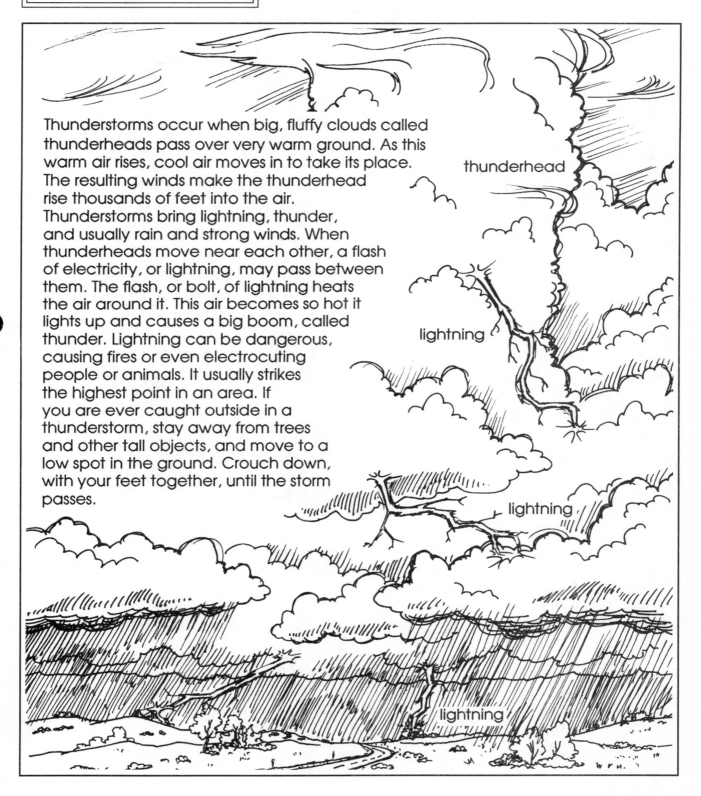

Thunderstorms occur when big, fluffy clouds called thunderheads pass over very warm ground. As this warm air rises, cool air moves in to take its place. The resulting winds make the thunderhead rise thousands of feet into the air. Thunderstorms bring lightning, thunder, and usually rain and strong winds. When thunderheads move near each other, a flash of electricity, or lightning, may pass between them. The flash, or bolt, of lightning heats the air around it. This air becomes so hot it lights up and causes a big boom, called thunder. Lightning can be dangerous, causing fires or even electrocuting people or animals. It usually strikes the highest point in an area. If you are ever caught outside in a thunderstorm, stay away from trees and other tall objects, and move to a low spot in the ground. Crouch down, with your feet together, until the storm passes.

thunderhead

lightning

lightning

lightning

Name _____

Tornadoes

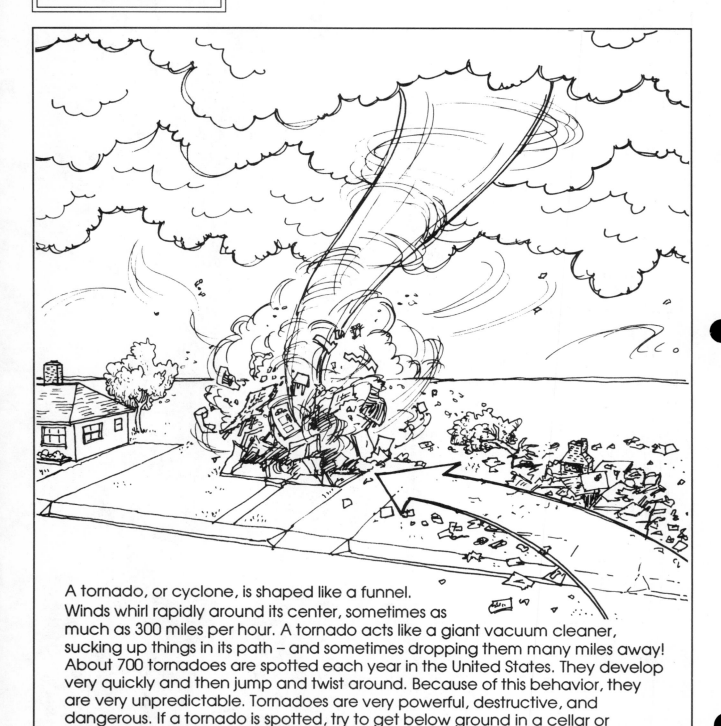

A tornado, or cyclone, is shaped like a funnel. Winds whirl rapidly around its center, sometimes as much as 300 miles per hour. A tornado acts like a giant vacuum cleaner, sucking up things in its path – and sometimes dropping them many miles away! About 700 tornadoes are spotted each year in the United States. They develop very quickly and then jump and twist around. Because of this behavior, they are very unpredictable. Tornadoes are very powerful, destructive, and dangerous. If a tornado is spotted, try to get below ground in a cellar or basement until the danger is over.

Name _____

Hurricanes

Hurricanes begin over the ocean. Whirling winds begin to blow and grow in strength. Hurricanes are usually 300 to 400 miles wide. The rain, high winds, and huge ocean waves they bring sometimes sink ships, cause floods, and destroy buildings on islands and along the coast. Because hurricanes develop slowly, the National Weather Service can usually predict their movement and provide warnings to people living in the path. If a hurricane is on the way, people are asked to evacuate their homes and move farther inland until the storm is over.

Name _____

Rainbow Haiku

red
orange
yellow
green
blue
purple

Name

_____

_____

Big Dipper
_____

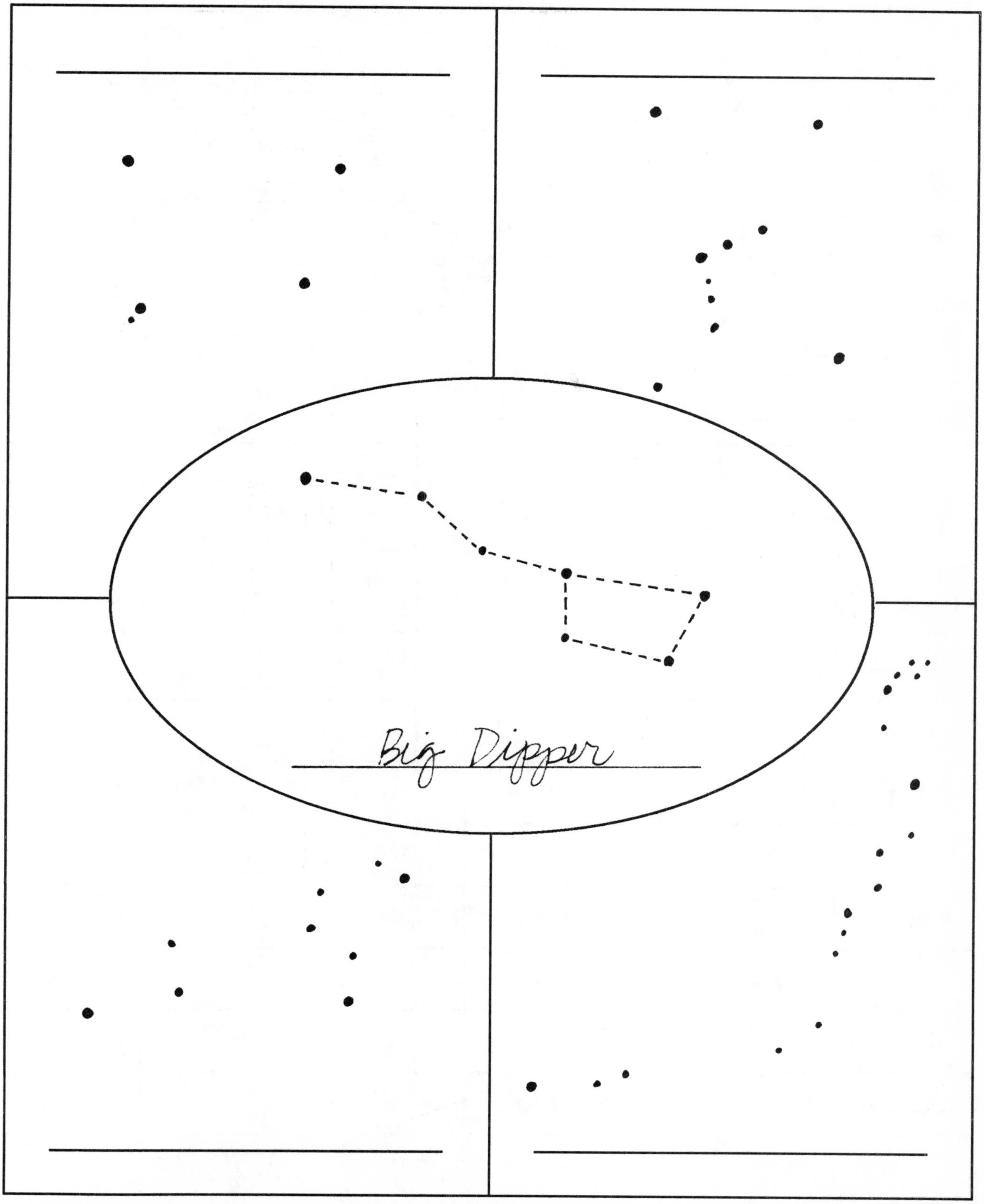

_____

_____

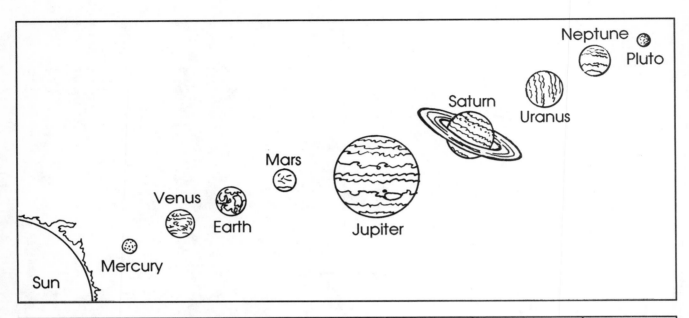

Planet	Color	Number of moons	Approximate rotation time	Approximate revolution time	Distance from the sun	Diameter
Mercury	Dark gray	0	1,407 hours	83 days	36,000,000 miles	3,010 miles
Venus	Silver	0	5,832 hours	224 days	67,200,000 miles	7,620 miles
Earth	Blue	1	24 hours	365 days	92,956,524 miles	7,926 miles
Mars	Red	2	24 1/2 hours	687 days	142,000,000 miles	4,220 miles
Jupiter	Light yellow	22 or more	10 hours	4,329 days	484,000,000 miles	88,800 miles
Saturn	Yellow	21 or more	10 1/2 hours	10,753 days	886,000,000 miles	74,000 miles
Uranus	Blue-green	15 or more	11 hours	30,660 days	1,780,000,000 miles	29,500 miles
Neptune	Blue-green	2	16 hours	59,860 days	2,800,000,000 miles	27,200 miles
Pluto	Unknown	1	6 1/2 hours	90,410 days	3,660,000,000 miles	3,600 miles

SPACE EXPLORERS

For 300 years after Galileo lived, people continued to study space and dream about space travel. But when space travel really began in 1960, animals were the first to be sent up. Two dogs named Strelka and Belka spent a whole day in space. They came back to earth by parachute.

3

Galileo was an astronomer and teacher who was born in 1564. He never traveled in space, but he constructed one of the first telescopes and used it to study space. He believed the earth moved around the sun. Other people did not agree with him. He was arrested and ordered to stop talking about that idea. Now we know Galileo was right.

2

The first human to travel in space was a Soviet cosmonaut named Yuri Gagarin. In 1961, he made one orbit around the earth. His spacecraft traveled so fast he completed the trip in less than 2 hours.

4

In 1969, two American astronauts, Neil Armstrong and Ed Aldrin, went to the moon. They found gravity on the moon was so low that they were able to move very easily. They collected samples of moon rocks to bring back to earth.

5

New astronauts must study very hard, because living and working in space is very different from living and working on earth. In space, objects that are not tied down float around. Astronauts sometimes eat by squeezing foods into their mouth from a tube. They must understand their spaceship and all the controls on the instrument panel, and they must be able to solve problems quickly.

7

Since that time, much has been learned about space and about how space can be useful to people on earth. More and more young men and women are becoming astronauts. Sally Ride was the first American woman and Guion Bluford was the first African-American to become astronauts.

6

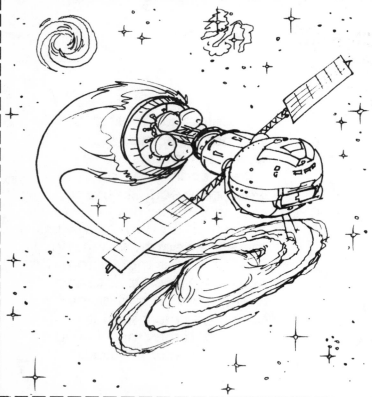

Astronauts and scientists are learning new things about space all the time. What do you think they will learn about next in space? What kinds of space equipment will be built? Where do you think spaceships, with or without astronauts to guide them, will go? Will life be discovered on other planets? These are exciting things to think about.

8

Apollo and Phaeton

Retold by: _____

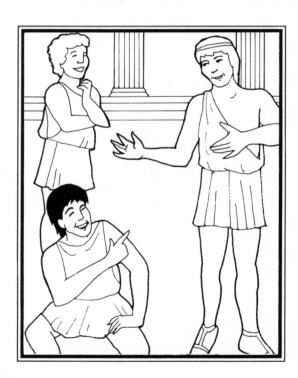

_____
_____
_____
_____
_____
_____
_____
_____
_____

3

_____

_____

_____

_____

_____

_____

_____

_____

_____

2

_____

_____

_____

_____

_____

_____

_____

_____

_____

4

_____
_____
_____
_____
_____
_____
_____
_____
_____

5

_____
_____
_____
_____
_____
_____
_____
_____
_____

7

6

8

_____
_____
_____
_____
_____
_____
_____
_____
_____

9

DISCARD

_____
_____
_____
_____
_____
_____
_____
_____
_____

10

DISCARD

The Myth of Proserpina

Retold by: _____

_____
_____
_____

3

_____

_____

_____

2

_____

_____

_____

4

5

7

_____
_____
_____

6

_____
_____
_____

8

Name _____

_____
_____
_____

9

_____
_____
_____

11

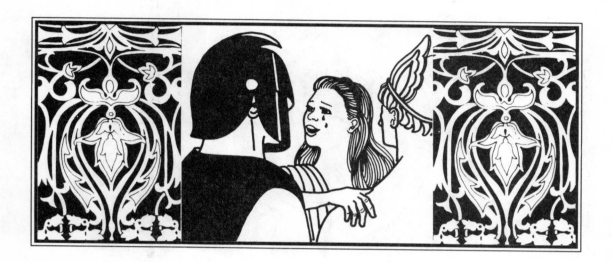

_____
_____
_____

10

_____
_____
_____

12

_____

_____

_____

13

DISCARD

Name _____

_____

_____

_____

14

DISCARD

Name _____

With your partner, list several ways in which families of long ago met their basic needs and how families meet the same needs today.

Family 100 years ago   Family today

Food

Water

Shelter

Clothing

Other
